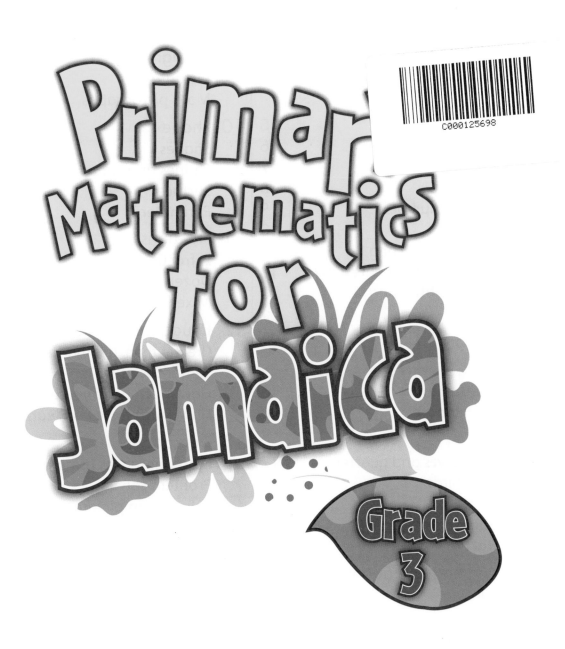

Primary Mathematics for Jamaica

Grade 3

Agatha James and Sheyla Constantine

Revised by Catherine V Malcolm for the
new integrated Jamaican curriculum

Contents

About this book 4

1 Working with 2-digit and 3-digit numbers
Ordering numbers 5
Adding and subtracting 6
Adding 2-digit numbers 7
More adding 8
Working with numbers 9
Place value 10
Adding and subtracting 11
Rounding off to the nearest 10 12
Adding and subtracting 13

2 Pictographs
A pictograph 14

3 Measuring length
More measuring 15
Measuring length 16

4 Fractions
Fractions: halves and quarters 17
Fractions: thirds 18
$\frac{1}{2}$, $\frac{1}{3}$ and $\frac{1}{4}$ 19
More about fractions 20
More fractions 21

5 Counting and operations
Skip counting 22
Money 23
Word and number problems 24
Addition and subtraction facts 25
Looking back 26
Looking back 27

6 Fractions
Naming fractions 28
Comparing fractions 29
Equivalent fractions 30
More about equivalent fractions 31
Unit fractions 32

7 Measurement – mixed
Units of length 33
Grams and kilograms 34
Capacity 35
The calendar 36

8 Money
Rounding off prices 37
Money 38

9 Pictographs
Pictographs 39
More pictographs 40

10 Shape
Shapes 41
Shapes around us 42
Surfaces 43
Perimeter 44

11 Fractions
A fraction of a set 45
Dozen 46
Mixed numbers 47

12 Equations and inequalities
Greater than, less than, equal to 48
Sentences using n 49
How much have you learned? 50
How much have you learned? 51

13 Operations
More sentences using n 52
Problem-solving 53
Subtraction pictures 54

14 Measurement
Working with lengths 55
Estimating perimeter 56
Metres and centimetres 57
Measurement 58

15 Fractions
Fractions 59

16 Multiplication
Multiplying 60
More multiplying 61
Multiplication facts 62
Multiplying bigger numbers 63
Multiplying by 0 64
Operations 65

17 Time
Calculating age 66

18 Measuring temperature
Temperature 67

19 Number operations
Adding and multiplying 68
Multiplying 69
Multiplying by 3 70

Multiplication game	71	
Multiplying	72	
Multiplying by 10	73	
Dividing by 1 or 0	74	
Multiplication: $7 \times 1 = 1 \times 7$	75	
Multiplying 2-digit numbers	76	
Multiplying and regrouping	77	
Multiplying bigger numbers	78	
Estimating products	79	
Comparing products	80	
Looking back	81	
Looking back	82	

20 Lines, paths and shapes
Open and closed figures	83
Lines, rays and line segments	84
Rays, angles and square corners	85
Angles and right angles	86
Simple closed paths	87

21 Collecting and representing data
Using tally marks	88
Bar graphs	89
Tables	90
Interpreting pictographs	91
More pictographs	92
Probability	93
Collecting and recording data	94
How much have you learned?	95
How much have you learned?	96

22 Number operations
True or false	97
Multiplying and dividing	98
Multiplication and division game	99
More operations	100

23 Capacity
Comparing litre amounts	101

24 Time
Time on the hour and half-hour	102
Time on the quarter-hour	103
Quarter past, quarter to	104
Telling time in 5-minute intervals	105

25 Fractions
Fractions – part of a set	106
Unit fractions	107

26 Money
Coins	108
Problem-solving	109

Using money	110
Making change	111
Calculating with money	112
Spending money	113

27 Word search
Find the word	114

28 Data handling
Working with data	115
Collecting data about living things	116
Using data	117

29 Division
Division	118
Division	119
Division	120
Division	121
Division by subtracting	122
Division	123
Division on a number line	124
Looking back	125
Looking back	126

30 Number patterns
Number patterns	127

31 Geometry
Naming polygons	128

32 Probability
Probability	129
Probability	130

33 Measurement
Measuring with square units	131
Working with km	132

34 Number operations
Division at work	133
Division problems	134
Dividing bigger numbers	135
More division with bigger numbers	136
Multiplying and dividing	137
More division	138

35 Problem-solving
Story problems	139
Make up an additional statement	140
More problem-solving	141
How much have you learned?	142
How much have you learned?	143

About this book

Introducing *Primary Mathematics for Jamaica*

This well-known series has been revised and rewritten by a team of dedicated educators from Jamaica. Changes have been made to incorporate the integrated Jamaican curriculum and to provide for the needs and desires of pupils in an ever-changing world. In addition, the books help to foster both individual and group learning, preparing the child for the world of today and the future.

This book is the third in the series. It will encourage children to learn, experiment and find out more about mathematics in the environment around them. To this end, it provides both formal and informal activities and ideas to make learning both enjoyable and rewarding.

The *Primary Mathematics for Jamaica* series helps children to build on and strengthen their understanding of mathematical concepts. The series uses a spiral approach to learning – concepts are introduced, explained, practised and reinforced at regular intervals. This ensures that each pupil can build on and clarify his or her understanding of the basic mathematical concepts.

In Grade 3, the pupil is provided with a colourful Workbook that provides a refreshing and enjoyable guide to the world of numeracy, using familiar examples from daily Jamaican life. A Teacher's Guide accompanies the Workbook for each grade.

Features of the Workbook include:
- **Problem-solving opportunities** which challenge children to think about concepts they have learned in mathematics in more abstract ways.
- **Talk about** points which encourage children to make links between mathematics and the real world and to verbalise and communicate their ideas.
- **Literacy support** in the form of activities that develop reading, writing, speaking and listening skills. These are indicated by ✏.
- **Interactive group activities** which encourage children to process information and pose their own questions about their learning.
- **Practical activities** which encourage children to use resources and materials to make and do things that involve applying mathematics in the real world. These activities are indicated by ✋.
- **Looking back pages** which serve to review material taught and which can be used in continuous assessment.
- **How much have you learned?** pages which can be used for formal assessment, allowing teachers to assess how well children are coping with concepts and to evaluate which areas need more attention.

More detailed guidelines for teaching each topic can be found in the Teacher's Guide for each grade. The full scope of topics covered in each Workbook can be seen in the table of contents on pages 2 and 3.

Ordering numbers

1 The tickets on these strips are numbered in order. Fill in the missing ticket numbers.

a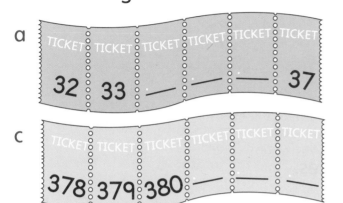

32 33 ___ ___ ___ 37

b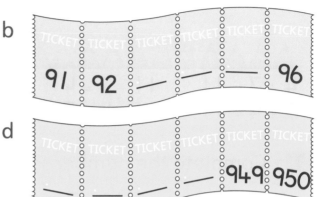

91 92 ___ ___ ___ 96

c

378 379 380 ___ ___ ___

d

___ ___ ___ 949 950

2 These seats are also numbered in order. Fill in the seat number before and after.

a

107

b

529

c

892

d

963

3 Fill in the missing numbers.

a 107, 108, ___, ___, ___, 112, 113   b 276, 277, ___, ___, ___, 281

c ___, ___, ___, ___, 218, 219   d ___, ___, ___, 735, 736, 737

e ___, ___, ___, ___, 449, 450   f 660, 670, 680, ___, ___, ___

4 Rewrite the numbers in order, smallest first.

a

400 370 350 380 360 390

b

821 781 811 771 791 801

c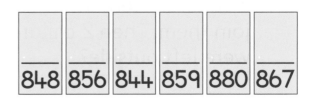

364 374 368 370 372 366

d

848 856 844 859 880 867

Adding and subtracting

Remember, $7 + 6 =$ △△△△△△△ + △△△△△△

$7 + 6 = 13$

△△△△△△△△△△△

$4 + 7 = 11$ $11 - 7 = 4$

$7 + 4 = 11$ $11 - 4 = 7$

1 Complete the number sentences.

a $5 + 7 = \underline{\quad}$ b $12 - 7 = \underline{\quad}$ c $7 - 5 = \underline{\quad}$ d $\underline{\quad} + 5 = 13$

e $9 + 6 = \underline{\quad}$ f $9 - 6 = \underline{\quad}$ g $15 - 9 = \underline{\quad}$ h $19 - \underline{\quad} = 1$

i $5 + 8 = \underline{\quad}$ j $8 + 9 = \underline{\quad}$ k $13 - 8 = \underline{\quad}$ l $\underline{\quad} - 5 = 14$

m $12 - 5 = \underline{\quad}$ n $15 - 6 = \underline{\quad}$ o $16 - 9 = \underline{\quad}$ p $7 + \underline{\quad} = 14$

2 Write a number sentence and an answer for each problem.

a Tom picked 7 mangoes. John picked 8 mangoes. How many mangoes did Tom and John pick altogether?

$\underline{\quad} + \underline{\quad} = \underline{\quad}$

b Mother bought 8 oranges and 6 grapefruits. How many fruits did she buy altogether?

$\underline{\quad} + \underline{\quad} = \underline{\quad}$

c There are 14 bananas in a bowl. Bob takes 5 bananas. How many bananas are left?

$\underline{\quad} + \underline{\quad} = \underline{\quad}$

d 3 children were in the school yard. 8 more children came to join them. Then 2 children went inside. How many children were left outside?

$\underline{\quad} + \underline{\quad} - \underline{\quad} = \underline{\quad}$

Adding 2-digit numbers

You can use tens and ones to help you add 2-digit numbers.
14 + 15 = ?

14 is one group of ten, and 4 ones.

15 is one group of ten, and 5 ones.

tens	ones
2 tens	9 ones

4 ones and 5 ones make 9 ones.
1 ten and 1 ten make 2 tens.
Now I have 2 tens and 9 ones or 29.

1   Add.

a

24 + 13 = ___

b

35 + 24 = ___

c

53 + 12 = ___

d

13 + 45 = ___

More adding

1. Add.

a

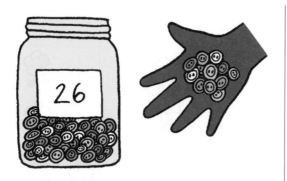

26 + 11 = ___

b

59 + 26 = ___

c

33 + 22 = ___

d

14 + 34 = ___

2. Marcus scored **23** runs in a cricket match. Laura scored **15** runs. How many runs did Marcus and Laura score altogether?

_____

3. Joan got **34** marks in her first test. She got **25** marks in her second test. How many marks did she get in total?

_____

4. Sadie and Ben collected bottle caps to make a shaker. Sadie collected **62** bottle caps. Ben collected **57** bottle caps. How many did they collect altogether?

_____

Working with numbers

1 Fill in the table. Show your partner the number on a calculator.

	hundreds	tens	ones	number
a	||	||||||		260
b	|	|||	||	
c	||||	|||||	||||	
d	||||||	||||||	|	
e	||||||||	||	|||	

2 Circle the greatest number in each set. Write it in words in your exercise book.

a   105, 375, 299   b   500, 700, 200   c   95, 100, 210
d   613, 361, 163   e   227, 272, 722   f   457, 710, 601

3 Circle the smallest number in each set. Write it in words in your exercise book.

a   120, 273, 112   b   92, 79, 85   c   950, 960, 940
d   706, 802, 505   e   445, 501, 800   f   100, 35, 60

Where do we use machines to help us work with numbers?

Place value

hundreds	tens	ones
||	|||	|||||

2 hundreds 3 tens 5 ones
200 + 30 + 5 = 235

hundreds	tens	ones
||||||		

6 hundreds 0 tens 0 ones
600 + 0 + 0 = 600

hundreds	tens	ones
||	|||||||	

2 hundreds 7 tens 0 ones
200 + 70 + 0 = 270

hundreds	tens	ones
||||		||||||||

4 hundreds 0 tens 8 ones
400 + 0 + 8 = 408

1   Fill in the number sentences.

a
hundreds	tens	ones
||||	||	||||||

____ hundreds ____ tens ____ ones

____ + ____ + ____ = ____

b
hundreds	tens	ones
|||||	|||	

____ hundreds ____ tens ____ ones

____ + ____ + ____ = ____

c
hundreds	tens	ones
|		||||||

____ hundreds ____ tens ____ ones

____ + ____ + ____ = ____

d
hundreds	tens	ones
||||||||		

____ hundreds ____ tens ____ ones

____ + ____ + ____ = ____

Adding and subtracting

1 Find the total for each sum. The first example has been done for you.

a
$$\begin{array}{r} 32 \\ + 12 \\ \hline 44 \end{array}$$

b
$$\begin{array}{r} 35 \\ + 14 \\ \hline \end{array}$$

c
$$\begin{array}{r} 21 \\ + 11 \\ \hline \end{array}$$

d
$$\begin{array}{r} 64 \\ + 25 \\ \hline \end{array}$$

e
$$\begin{array}{r} 43 \\ + 25 \\ \hline \end{array}$$

f
$$\begin{array}{r} 31 \\ + 18 \\ \hline \end{array}$$

g
$$\begin{array}{r} 44 \\ + 22 \\ \hline \end{array}$$

h
$$\begin{array}{r} 24 \\ + 23 \\ \hline \end{array}$$

2 Complete the sums. The numbers you need are shown on the shapes.

a 32 14 46
$32 + 14 =$ _____
$46 - 14 =$ _____
$46 - 32 =$ _____

b 7 11 18
$7 + 11 =$ _____
_____ $- 11 = 7$
$18 - 7 =$ _____

c 16 20 36
$20 + 16 =$ _____
$36 -$ _____ $= 20$
$36 - 20 =$ _____

d 43 65 22
$43 + 22 =$ _____
$65 - 22 =$ _____
$65 -$ _____ $= 22$

e 59 26 33
$26 + 33 =$ _____
$59 - 33 =$ _____
$59 -$ _____ $= 33$

f 39 17 22
$17 + 22 =$ _____
_____ $- 22 = 17$
_____ $- 17 = 22$

What relationship between adding and subtracting can you see in the sums above?

Rounding off to the nearest 10

Sometimes we round off numbers to make them easier to work with. When you round off to the nearest 10:
- If the ones digit is 1, 2, 3 or 4, change it to 0: 53 → 50
- If the ones digit is 5, 6, 7, 8 or 9, change it to 0 and add 1 to the tens digit: 57 → 60

Liz watched TV for **22** minutes – about **20** minutes.
87 people watched the football – about **90** people.
The shopkeeper sold **421** sodas – about **420** sodas.

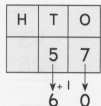

H	T	O
	5	7

+1
6 0

	2	2

2 0

	8	7

+1
9 0

4	2	1

4 2 0

1 Round off to the nearest 10.

a Joe ran for **18** minutes.
About ___ minutes.

b Sarah ran for **33** minutes.
About ___ minutes.

c Steven ran for **12** minutes.
About ___ minutes.

d Gloria ran for **44** minutes.
About ___ minutes.

2 Round off to the nearest 10.

a

142 people came to the wedding.
About ___ people.

b

788 people watched the parade.
About ___ people.

c

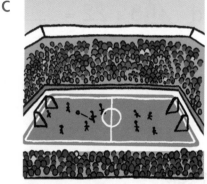

975 people watched the football.
About ___ people.

Adding and subtracting

Daniel used rounding off to help him add big numbers quickly. Read what he did.

$$29 + 40 = 69$$
$$30 + 40 = 70$$
$$70 - 1 = 69$$

First he rounded off 29 to 30.
(29 + 1 = 30)
30 + 40 = 70
Then he subtracted the 1 that he added to round off.
70 – 1 = 69

Can you think of another easy way to work out 29 + 40?

Here is another example:
32 + 41   Round off and add. 30 + 40 = 70
Then add the (2 + 1) that you took away when you rounded off.
70 + 3 = 73

1 Round off to the nearest ten.

a   99   b   419   c   58   d   179   e   844

2 Circle the correct answer from the brackets.

a   30 – 16 = (46, 16, 14)   b   24 + 15 = (39, 31, 40)
c   28 + 43 = (60, 71, 25)   d   40 – 18 = (30, 38, 22)
e   60 – 17 = (25, 43, 35)   f   29 + 38 = (70, 67, 9)
g   50 – 19 = (69, 30, 31)   h   22 + 17 = (30, 39, 35)

3 Use rounding off to help you solve.

a   71 – 48   b   33 + 21   c   89 – 71
d   39 – 11   e   18 + 19   f   42 + 49

Solve this riddle.
One of my digits is 3 more than the other. One of my factors is 2. What number am I?

Unit 2 A pictograph

1 Four children collected empty tins.
The pictograph shows how many
tins they collected.

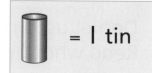 = 1 tin

Empty tins collected

Bella	(11 tins)
Marcus	(15 tins)
Tom	(9 tins)
Laura	(7 tins)

Answer the questions using the pictograph.
a   How many tins did Tom collect?
b   How many tins did Laura collect?
c   Who collected the most tins?
d   Who collected the least tins?
e   How many more tins did Marcus collect than Bella?
f   How many tins did the four children collect altogether?

2 Work in groups. Collect empty tins or jars for your classroom.
When everyone has collected some, draw pictographs on
paper to show how many each group member collected.

3 A recycling organisation pays $25 for a kilogram of used tins.
A school wants each child to raise $200 by collecting tins.
How many kilograms of tins must each child bring to do this?

Why is it important to recycle tins?
How can people make money from recycling tins?

More measuring

1 Name some of these things used for measuring.

_____ _____ _____

2 For each object, choose whether to measure in cm or m and fill in column 2. Guess the length and fill in column 3. Then measure and fill in column 4.

Object	cm or m	length (guess)	length (measure)
classroom door			
pencil			
paperclip			
schoolyard			
this book			
your copybook			
a leaf			
blackboard			

Measuring length

1 What would you use to measure the length of each item? Write centimetres or metres.

 a

 b

 c

_____   _____   _____

 d

 e

 f

_____   _____   _____

2 How tall are you?

a   Stand next to five friends. Guess how tall each one is (include yourself). Fill in column **2**.

b   Now measure each one (include yourself). Fill in column **3**.

Name	Height (guess)	Height (measure)

100 cm = 1 metre

Fractions: halves and quarters

1 Tick the shapes that have $\frac{1}{2}$ shaded. Draw a circle around the shapes that have $\frac{1}{4}$ shaded.

a   b   c   d   e

f   g   h   i   j

Fill in $\frac{1}{2}$ or $\frac{1}{4}$:

____ of the girls are wearing skirts. ____ of the children are wearing shorts. ____ of the children have a pet. ____ of the children are girls and ____ of the children are boys. ____ of the girls have short hair. ____ of the children are wearing jeans. ____ of the children are wearing glasses. ____ of the boys are dressed for running.

3 Shade $\frac{1}{2}$ of each set. Then draw crosses in $\frac{1}{4}$ of each set.

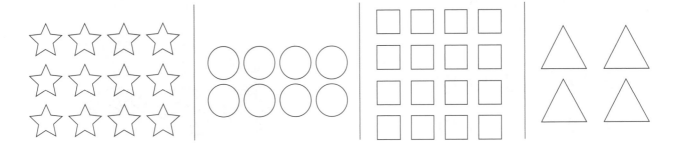

Fractions: thirds

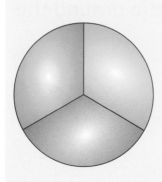 How many equal parts is the circle divided into? When something is divided into three, each equal part is called one-third or $\frac{1}{3}$.

We give the parts of a fraction names.

$\frac{1}{3}$ ← **numerator** – the number of parts we are working with

← **denominator** – the total number of parts in the whole

1 Shade $\frac{1}{3}$ of each shape.

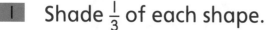

2 Count how many. Then circle $\frac{2}{3}$ of each set.

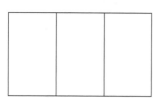

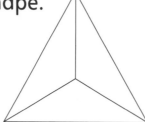

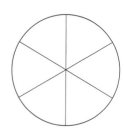

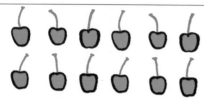

$\frac{1}{2}$, $\frac{1}{3}$ and $\frac{1}{4}$

1   a   Colour red the shapes that show $\frac{1}{2}$ (halves).

     b   Colour blue the shapes that show $\frac{1}{3}$ (thirds).

     c   Colour green the shapes that show $\frac{1}{4}$ (quarters).

2   a   Shade $\frac{1}{2}$ of each set yellow.   b   Colour $\frac{1}{3}$ of each set red.   c   Colour $\frac{1}{4}$ of each set blue.

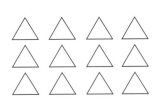
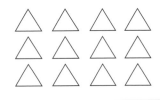
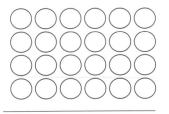
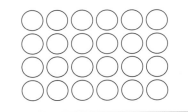
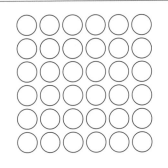
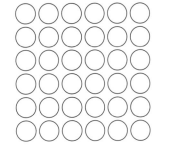
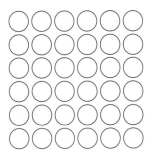

More about fractions

A fraction that has 1 as its numerator is called a **unit fraction**. We can sort unit fractions into families according to their denominators. For example, in the fraction family of $\frac{1}{2}$, all the fractions have denominators that are multiples of 2.

Fraction family of $\frac{1}{2}$	Fraction family of $\frac{1}{3}$	Fraction family of $\frac{1}{5}$
$\frac{1}{2}$	$\frac{1}{3}$	$\frac{1}{5}$
$\frac{1}{4}$	$\frac{1}{6}$	$\frac{1}{10}$
$\frac{1}{6}$	$\frac{1}{9}$	$\frac{1}{15}$
$\frac{1}{8}$	$\frac{1}{12}$	$\frac{1}{20}$

1 Decide which family each fraction belongs to. Write the fractions in the correct column of the table above.

$$\frac{1}{16} \qquad \frac{1}{15} \qquad \frac{1}{27} \qquad \frac{1}{24} \qquad \frac{1}{32} \qquad \frac{1}{125}$$

2 Write three unit fractions that fit into both the fraction family of $\frac{1}{2}$ and the fraction family of $\frac{1}{3}$. Look at the table above to help you.

Look at this fraction: $\frac{2}{3}$. The numerator is smaller than the denominator, so we call this fraction a **proper fraction**.

Look at this fraction: $\frac{4}{3}$. The numerator is larger than the denominator, so we call this fraction an **improper fraction**.

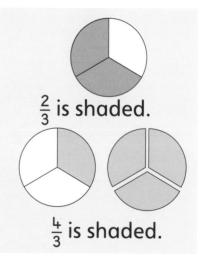

$\frac{2}{3}$ is shaded.

$\frac{4}{3}$ is shaded.

3 a Circle the proper fractions below in blue.
   b Circle the improper fractions below in red.

$$\frac{7}{8} \qquad \frac{9}{10} \qquad \frac{11}{4} \qquad \frac{3}{2} \qquad \frac{8}{9} \qquad \frac{10}{7} \qquad \frac{4}{5} \qquad \frac{5}{4}$$

More fractions

1   a   Colour one part of each shape.

       b   Write X next to shapes that have $\frac{1}{4}$ shaded.

       c   Write Y next to shapes that have $\frac{1}{2}$ shaded.

       d   Write Z next to shapes that have $\frac{1}{6}$ shaded.

2   Draw the fractions of each set. Write the answer.

a $\frac{1}{2}$ of  =   = 5

b $\frac{1}{3}$ of  =   = ___

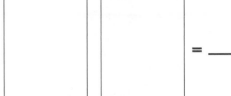

c $\frac{1}{4}$ of  =   = ___

Skip counting

1 Count in 10s. Fill in the missing numbers.

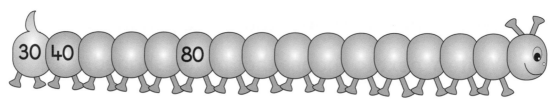

30 40 80

2 Count in 5s. Fill in the missing numbers.

150 175 180 185

3 Count in 20s. Fill in the missing numbers.

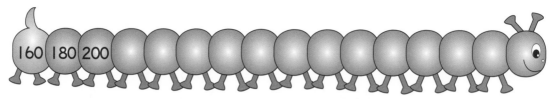

160 180 200

4 Count in 25s. Fill in the missing numbers.

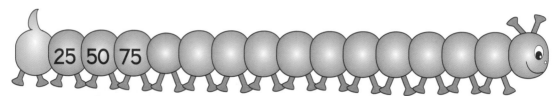

25 50 75

5 Count in 25s. Join the dots.

225 ●Start here
25
175● 200 ●
●50
●75
●100
●150
●125

Money

1 How much? Write the amount.

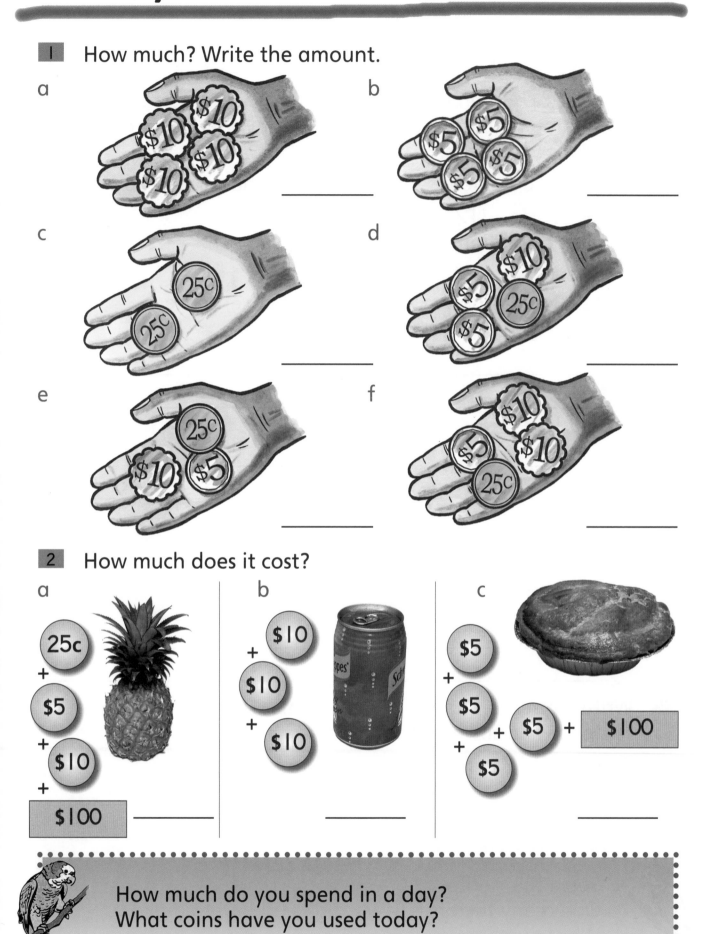

a

b

c

d

e

f

2 How much does it cost?

a

b

c

How much do you spend in a day?
What coins have you used today?

Word and number problems

This is a word problem:

There are 12 children in Angela's group. The teacher sends 4 more children to join the group. How many children are there in the group altogether?

We can write a number sentence to solve the word problem.

$12 + 4 =$ _____ $12 + 4 = 16$
There are 16 children altogether.

1 Write a word problem for each number sentence.

   a $5 + 7 =$ _____

_____

_____

   b $6 + 4 =$ _____

_____

_____

   c $8 + 3 =$ _____

_____

_____

   d $9 + 4 =$ _____

_____

_____

2 Write a question for these statements. Then write the number sentence and solve the problem.

Susan had 12 pencils. She gave 5 to Mark.

_____

_____

Solve this riddle.
One of my factors is 4. My digits add up to make 6.
What number am I?

Addition and subtraction facts

1 In the first house, add the number in the roof to each number in the blue column. Circle the correct answer in the white column. In the second house, subtract. The first one has been done for you in each house.

+15

16	41, (31)
23	48, 38
18	43, 33
19	44, 34
27	32, 42
21	35, 36
28	45, 43
17	32, 42
29	44, 34
26	41, 51

−20

31	29, (11)
39	21, 19
33	21, 13
37	20, 17
40	20, 22
38	18, 22
36	16, 32
32	30, 12
30	10, 20
29	19, 9

2 Exchange books with a partner. Write twelve addition sums using any numbers up to 50. Then get your own book back. Who can finish all their sums correctly the fastest?

_____   _____   _____

_____   _____   _____

_____   _____   _____

_____   _____   _____

Solve these riddles.
- Our product is 12. We add up to 7. What numbers are we?
- I am 4 more than the sum of 8 and 3. What number am I?

Looking back

1 Write each set of numbers from smallest to biggest.

a

752	527	257	725	275	572
___	___	___	___	___	___

b

918	981	819	189	891	198
___	___	___	___	___	___

2 Mike is going shopping. How much does each set of items cost? Write the number sentence and the answer.

a
$82 $25

b
$25 $82

c
$30 $35

d
$42 $20

3 Work out these.

79	54	29	45	88	68
− 55	− 33	− 17	− 12	− 33	− 25

99	28	19	76	82	54
− 55	− 25	− 9	− 63	− 11	− 14

Looking back

 4 At Michelle's party, there were 13 red balloons, 11 blue balloons and 15 green balloons. Fill in the pictograph.

Balloons at Michelle's party

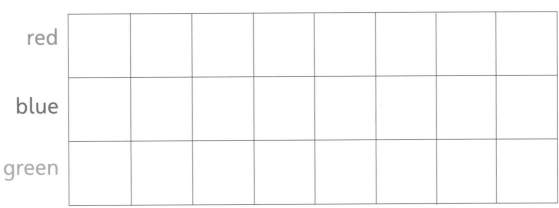

red							
blue							
green							

 = 2 balloons

a How many red balloons were there? _____

b How many more green balloons than blue balloons were there? _____

c How many balloons were there altogether? _____

 5 In each of the fractions, circle the fraction that does not belong in the same family as the others.

a $\frac{1}{4}$ $\frac{1}{8}$ $\frac{1}{5}$ $\frac{1}{12}$ b $\frac{1}{7}$ $\frac{1}{3}$ $\frac{1}{6}$ $\frac{1}{12}$ c $\frac{1}{2}$ $\frac{1}{4}$ $\frac{1}{6}$ $\frac{1}{5}$

d $\frac{1}{7}$ $\frac{1}{2}$ $\frac{1}{14}$ $\frac{1}{21}$ e $\frac{1}{3}$ $\frac{1}{9}$ $\frac{1}{4}$ $\frac{1}{18}$ f $\frac{1}{2}$ $\frac{1}{5}$ $\frac{1}{10}$ $\frac{1}{15}$

 6 Write whether you would measure it in cm or m.

   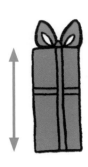

_____ _____ _____ _____

Naming fractions

2 out of 4 are shaded. $\frac{2}{4}$

numerator – names the shaded part

denominator – names the number of equal parts in the whole

1 What fraction is shaded? Fill in the denominator or the numerator to complete the fraction.

a

$\frac{1}{\Box}$

b

$\frac{1}{\Box}$

c

$\frac{\Box}{4}$

d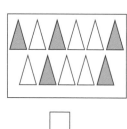

$\frac{\Box}{11}$

e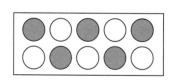

$\frac{5}{\Box}$

f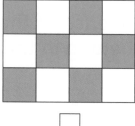

$\frac{\Box}{12}$

2 Draw pictures to show these fractions.

a $\frac{4}{10}$ b $\frac{5}{11}$ c $\frac{7}{12}$

d $\frac{1}{8}$ e $\frac{3}{12}$ f $\frac{8}{15}$

Comparing fractions

 $\frac{1}{2}$ $\frac{1}{4}$ 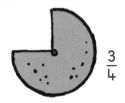 $\frac{3}{4}$

1   a   Circle the biggest piece of orange.

      b   Underline the smallest piece of orange.

2   Fill in < (less than), > (greater than) or =. The first one has been done for you.

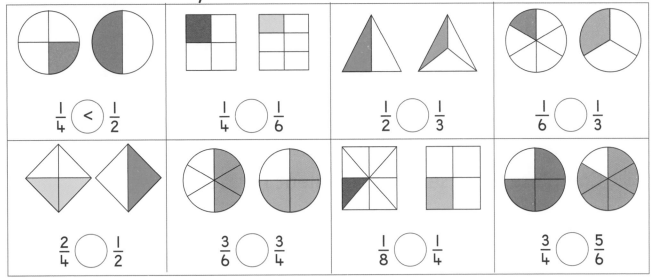

$\frac{1}{4}$ < $\frac{1}{2}$	$\frac{1}{4}$ ◯ $\frac{1}{6}$	$\frac{1}{2}$ ◯ $\frac{1}{3}$	$\frac{1}{6}$ ◯ $\frac{1}{3}$
$\frac{2}{4}$ ◯ $\frac{1}{2}$	$\frac{3}{6}$ ◯ $\frac{3}{4}$	$\frac{1}{8}$ ◯ $\frac{1}{4}$	$\frac{3}{4}$ ◯ $\frac{5}{6}$

3   Use drawings to help you fill in the correct answer (<, > or =).

a $\frac{1}{4}$ ◯ $\frac{1}{2}$ b $\frac{1}{3}$ ◯ $\frac{1}{6}$ c $\frac{1}{4}$ ◯ $\frac{1}{3}$ d $\frac{1}{3}$ ◯ $\frac{1}{2}$

e $\frac{1}{4}$ ◯ $\frac{1}{2}$ f $\frac{1}{6}$ ◯ $\frac{1}{4}$ g $\frac{1}{2}$ ◯ $\frac{1}{6}$ h $\frac{1}{3}$ ◯ $\frac{2}{6}$

Equivalent fractions

Look at this fraction wall and answer the questions below.

$\frac{1}{2}$		$\frac{1}{2}$	

The fraction wall shows rows divided into: $\frac{1}{2}$, $\frac{1}{3}$, $\frac{1}{4}$, $\frac{1}{5}$, $\frac{1}{6}$, $\frac{1}{8}$, $\frac{1}{10}$, $\frac{1}{12}$.

0 ← ——————————————————————— → 1

1 Complete these sets of equivalent fractions.

a $\dfrac{1}{2} = \dfrac{}{4} = \dfrac{}{8} = \dfrac{}{10}$ b $\dfrac{3}{4} = \dfrac{}{8} = \dfrac{}{12}$ c $\dfrac{2}{3} = \dfrac{}{6} = \dfrac{}{12}$

2 Explain in your own words why $\dfrac{6}{12} = \dfrac{1}{2}$. Use the fraction wall to help you.

_____

_____

_____

3 Fill in the following fractions at the correct positions on this number line: $\dfrac{1}{4}, \dfrac{1}{2}, \dfrac{3}{4}, \dfrac{7}{8}, \dfrac{3}{16}$

0 $\frac{1}{16}$ $\frac{2}{16}$ ←——————————————————————→ 1

More about equivalent fractions

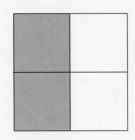

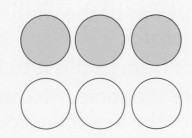

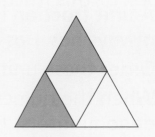

$\frac{1}{2} = \frac{2}{4}$

$\frac{1}{2} = \frac{3}{6}$

$\frac{1}{2} = \frac{2}{4}$

1 Write the equivalent fractions shown in each diagram.

a

$\frac{2}{3} = \frac{\square}{6}$

b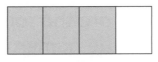

$\frac{6}{8} = \frac{\square}{4}$

c

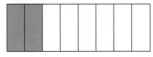

$\frac{1}{4} = \frac{\square}{8}$

d

$\frac{6}{10} = \frac{\square}{5}$

e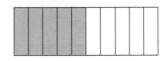

$\frac{1}{2} = \frac{\square}{\square}$

f

$1 = \frac{\square}{\square}$

g

$1 = \frac{\square}{5}$

h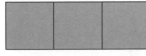

$\frac{2}{2} = \frac{\square}{3}$

i

$\frac{1}{2} = \frac{4}{\square}$

Unit fractions

A **unit fraction** is one part out of the whole. A unit fraction always has 1 as the numerator.

Order these unit fractions from smallest to largest: $\frac{1}{2}, \frac{1}{4}, \frac{1}{3}$

When the numerators are the same, we compare the denominators. The bigger the denominator, the smaller the fraction. Can you see why?

$\frac{1}{2}$ $\frac{1}{4}$ $\frac{1}{3}$

The correct order is: $\frac{1}{4} < \frac{1}{3} < \frac{1}{2}$

Order these fractions from smallest to largest: $\frac{4}{5}, \frac{3}{5}, \frac{1}{5}$

When the denominators are the same, we compare the numerators. The bigger the numerator, the bigger the fraction. Can you see why?

$\frac{4}{5}$ $\frac{3}{5}$ $\frac{1}{5}$

The correct order is: $\frac{1}{5} < \frac{3}{5} < \frac{4}{5}$

1   Fill in < or >.

a $\frac{1}{4} \bigcirc \frac{1}{12}$ b $\frac{1}{3} \bigcirc \frac{1}{2}$ c $\frac{1}{8} \bigcirc \frac{1}{12}$

d $\frac{1}{15} \bigcirc \frac{1}{17}$ e $\frac{1}{11} \bigcirc \frac{1}{6}$ f $\frac{1}{7} \bigcirc \frac{1}{14}$

2   Order each set of unit fractions from smallest to largest.

a $\frac{1}{4}, \frac{1}{3}, \frac{1}{5}$ _____   b $\frac{1}{7}, \frac{1}{3}, \frac{1}{4}$ _____   c $\frac{1}{2}, \frac{1}{5}, \frac{1}{6}$ _____

d $\frac{1}{5}, \frac{1}{7}, \frac{1}{12}$ _____   e $\frac{1}{5}, \frac{1}{4}, \frac{1}{20}$ _____   f $\frac{1}{5}, \frac{1}{2}, \frac{1}{3}$ _____

3   Fill in < or >.

a $\frac{2}{4} \bigcirc \frac{3}{4}$ b $\frac{3}{8} \bigcirc \frac{1}{8}$ c $\frac{7}{11} \bigcirc \frac{9}{11}$

d $\frac{12}{15} \bigcirc \frac{13}{15}$ e $\frac{8}{10} \bigcirc \frac{6}{10}$ f $\frac{1}{5} \bigcirc \frac{4}{5}$

4   Write each set of fractions in order from smallest to largest.

a $\frac{1}{4}, \frac{3}{4}, \frac{2}{4}$ _____   b $\frac{4}{6}, \frac{3}{6}, \frac{2}{6}$ _____   c $\frac{3}{5}, \frac{2}{5}, \frac{4}{5}$ _____

Units of length

Your teacher will give you a metre rule or a tape measure.

1 Guess the measurement of each object and fill in column 2. Then measure and fill in column 3.

Object	Guessed length	Actual length
teacher		
the tallest child in the class		
the shortest child in the class		
pencil		
desk		

The length around something is called the **perimeter**. You can use string to help you measure perimeter.

2 Use string to help you measure the perimeter of:
    a   a sock   b   a picture frame   c   a desk top

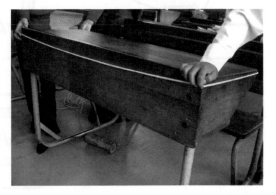

3 How long is a kilometre? What do we measure in kilometres?

Grams and kilograms

We measure mass in grams and kilograms.

1 a Which is heaviest?
b Which is lightest?

| 1 000 grams (g) = 1 kilogram (kg) |

c Order the items from lightest to heaviest.

lightest

heaviest

a b c d e

2 Look at the objects below. Under each object, write whether its mass is measured in kg or g. Estimate its mass.

Capacity

1   Three containers are filled from the same tap, one at a time.

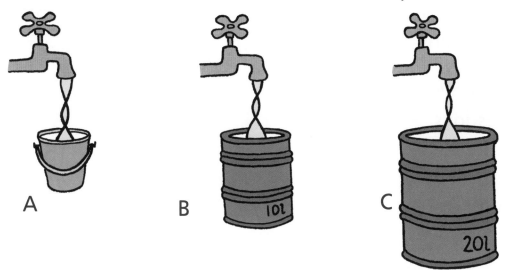

A   B   C

a   Which container will take longest to fill? _____

b   Underline the correct word:
The (*larger*, *smaller*) the container, the longer it takes to fill.

2   What would you use to fill these containers?
Circle the best choice.

a

b

c

3   The bucket holds 10 litres. The small cup holds $\frac{1}{8}$ of a litre
(125 ml). The large cup holds $\frac{1}{4}$ of a litre (250 ml).

a   How many small cups of
water fill the bucket? _____

b   How many large cups of
water fill the bucket? _____

c   How many of the small
cups fill the large cup? _____

The calendar

1   Look at the calendar and answer the questions.

a   January has ___ days.

b   How many are there in January?

     Mondays   ___

     Tuesdays   ___

     Fridays   ___

     Saturdays   ___

c   There are ___ school days in January.

d   There are ___ holidays in January.

e   The first day of January is a _____.

f   The last day is a _____.

g   The first day of the next month will be a _____.

h   The 8th day of February will be a _____.

JANUARY

Sun	Mon	Tue	Wed	Thur	Fri	Sat
	school starts		1	2	3	4
5	(6)	7	8	9	10	11
12	13	14	15	16	17	18
19	20	21	22	23	24	25
26	27	28	29	30	31	

2   Look at the calendar and answer the questions.

a   There are ___ days in June.

b   How many are there in June:

     Tuesdays   ___

     Wednesdays   ___

     Thursdays   ___

     Fridays   ___

     Sundays   ___

c   There are ___ school days in June.

d   There are ___ Mondays in June.

e   The first day of June is a _____.

f   The last day is a _____.

g   The first day of the next month will be a _____.

h   The 5th day of July will be a _____.

i   The 10th day of July will be a _____.

JUNE

Sun	Mon	Tue	Wed	Thur	Fri	Sat
		1	2	3	4	5	6
7	8	9	10	11	12	13
14	15	16	17 school closes	18	19	20
21	22	23	(24)	25	26	27
28	29	30				

Unit 8 Rounding off prices

1 You have already rounded numbers off to the nearest 10.

```
       4    12              28    37  43          55 59 62  68     77      85              99
◄──────┼─────┼──────────────┼─────┼───┼────────────┼────┼────┼─────┼───────┼──────────────┼───────►
   0      10     20     30     40     50     60     70     80     90    100
```

Look at the number line. Count in tens. Then look at the red numbers. Say which ten each number is closest to.

How to round off prices

Look at the ones.
Are there fewer than 5 ones?
Then change them to 0.

Are there 5 or more ones?
Then change them to 0 and
add an extra 10.

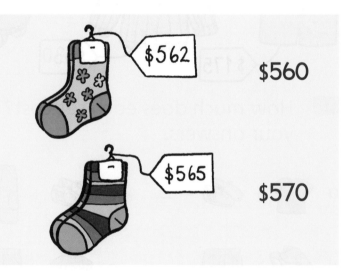

$562 → $560

$565 → $570

2 Round off each price to the nearest $10. Circle the correct answer.

$29 — $20, $30

$259 — $250, $260

$154 — $150, $160

$743 — $740, $750

$586 — $580, $590

$499 — $490, $500

$127 — $120, $130

$239 — $230, $240

$262 — $260, $270

3 Draw each exact price in coins and notes in your exercise book.

Money

1   How much does each set cost? Use a calculator to check your answers.

a   👕 + 👟 = ____   b   👟 + 👖 = ____   c   🧢 + 🛹 = ____

d   🎒 + 🩳 = ____   e   👕 + 🩳 = ____   f   🛹 + 🎒 = ____

2   John has $400. He buys 🎒. How much does he have left?

____ – ____ = ____

3   Sarah has $100. She buys 🧢. How much does she have left?

____ – ____ = ____

4   Nina has $700. She buys 👟 + 👖. How much does she have left?

____ + ____ = ____   ____ – ____ = ____

5   Mike has $350. He buys 🧢 + 🩳. How much does he have left?

____ + ____ = ____   ____ – ____ = ____

Pictographs

1 This pictograph shows the favourite colours of the pupils in a class.

Favourite colours

 = 4 pupils

a   Which colour do the most pupils like?   _____

b   How many pupils prefer blue?   _____

c   How many pupils prefer red?   _____

d   How many pupils prefer green?   _____

e   How many pupils prefer yellow?   _____

f   How many pupils are in this class altogether? _____

2   ⚲ = 5 girls   Draw pictures to show these numbers of girls.

10 girls	20 girls	25 girls

More pictographs

1   The pictograph shows the cakes that
four children bought at a cake sale.

= 1 cake

Ann	🧁 🧁 🧁 🧁 🧁
Julia	🧁 🧁 🧁
Ben	🧁 🧁 🧁 🧁 🧁 🧁
Andrew	🧁 🧁 🧁 🧁 🧁 🧁 🧁

a   Who bought the most cakes? _____
b   How many cakes did that child buy? _____
c   Who bought 2 cakes more than Julia? _____
d   Which two children bought 8 cakes altogether? _____
e   How many cakes did the four children buy altogether? _____

2   Sam, Bob and Kate picked mangoes. Sam picked
10 mangoes, Bob picked 6 mangoes, and Kate picked
7 mangoes. Fill in the pictograph to show how many they
picked. Don't forget to fill in the names.

_____

_____

_____

a   Who picked more than 9 mangoes? _____
b   Which two children picked fewer than 8 mangoes? _____
c   How many more mangoes did Kate pick than Bob? _____
d   Which two children picked 13 mangoes together? _____
e   How many mangoes did the three children pick
altogether? _____

Colour all the triangles red.
Colour all the squares blue.
Colour all the rectangles green.
Colour all the circles yellow.

 Design your own picture using only squares, triangles and circles.

Shapes around us

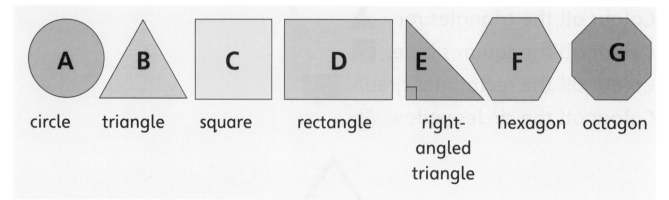

A circle   B triangle   C square   D rectangle   E right-angled triangle   F hexagon   G octagon

I   Match the shapes above to the objects in the pictures. Write the letters of the shapes you can see in each picture.

Surfaces

The outer faces of an object form its **surface**. The surfaces of solid shapes may be **flat** or **curved**. They may also have different textures, such as smooth, rough, bumpy or furry.

smooth, flat surface

smooth, curved surface

bumpy, curved surface

1 Describe the surface of each object. Use the words from the box.

| smooth | curved | shiny | rough | dry | sticky | spiky |

a

b

c

d

e

f

Perimeter

Perimeter is the distance around a shape or object. Both these shapes have a perimeter of **8** cm.

 1 Use string and a ruler to measure the perimeter of the following shapes.

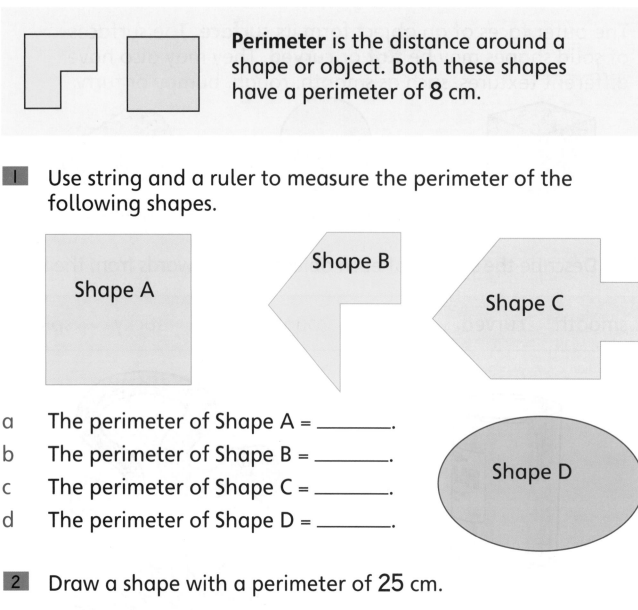

Shape A

Shape B

Shape C

Shape D

a   The perimeter of Shape A = _____.

b   The perimeter of Shape B = _____.

c   The perimeter of Shape C = _____.

d   The perimeter of Shape D = _____.

2 Draw a shape with a perimeter of **25** cm.

A fraction of a set

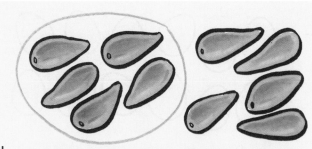 

$\frac{1}{2}$ of 10 mangoes = **5** mangoes $\frac{1}{2}$ of 8 mangoes = **4** mangoes

1 Circle half of each set. Write how many you have circled.

a    b

$\frac{1}{2}$ of 12 = ___ $\frac{1}{2}$ of 16 = ___

c    d

$\frac{1}{2}$ of 6 = ___ $\frac{1}{2}$ of 8 = ___

e    f

$\frac{1}{2}$ of ___ = ___ $\frac{1}{2}$ of ___ = ___

g  h

$\frac{1}{2}$ of ___ = ___ $\frac{1}{2}$ of ___ = ___

2 Look at the picture and complete the statements.

a $\frac{1}{\square}$ of the puppies are black.

b $\frac{\square}{\square}$ of the puppies are brown.

c $\frac{\square}{\square}$ of the puppies are spotted.

Dozen

A **dozen** is another word for 12.

A half-dozen = $\frac{1}{2}$ of 12 = 6

A quarter-dozen = $\frac{1}{4}$ of 12 = 3

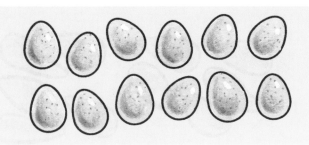

1 Draw more eggs to make a dozen of each.

a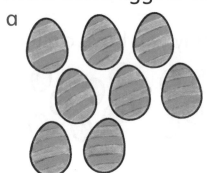

b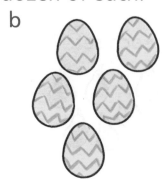

2 Circle the items that can be sold by the dozen.

sugar	eggs	meat	oranges	yams	callaloo
syrup	mangoes	carrots	bananas	milk	rice

3 a Sharon bought **2** dozen guineps. How many did she buy altogether? ____

b Michael bought 3 dozen mangoes. How many did he buy altogether? ____

4 a Draw a half-dozen bananas.

b Draw a quarter-dozen oranges.

Mixed numbers

We can write this fraction in different ways: $\frac{3}{3} + \frac{1}{3} = \frac{4}{3}$

1 whole + 1 third

A fraction with a numerator greater than its denominator is called an **improper fraction**.

We can write $\frac{4}{3}$ as a whole number and a fraction, like this:

$\frac{3}{3} = 1$

$1 + \frac{1}{3} = 1\frac{1}{3}$

So $\frac{4}{3} = 1\frac{1}{3}$

A fraction written as a whole number and a proper fraction is called a **mixed number**.

---

1 Write a mixed number to represent the total amount shaded in each diagram.

a

$\frac{2}{2} + \frac{1}{2} = $ _____

b

$\frac{4}{4} + \frac{1}{4} = $ _____

c

$\frac{2}{2} + \frac{2}{2} + \frac{1}{2} = $ _____

d

$\frac{3}{3} + \frac{2}{3} = $ _____

2 Draw pictures to show these mixed numbers.

a $2\frac{1}{4}$ b $1\frac{1}{3}$ c $3\frac{1}{5}$

Greater than, less than, equal to

Greater than >
4 > 3

Less than <
2 < 5

Equal to =
2 + 3 = 5

Remember, the open part of the < or > symbol always points to the bigger number.

1   Fill in the correct symbol (<, > or =) to make each number sentence true.

a   (6 + 5) ____ (5 + 6)   b   2 + (6 + 3) ____ (2 + 6) + 3

c   5 × 4 ____ 3 × 5   d   2 × 5 ____ 2 × 3

e   9 – 4 ____ 9 + 4   f   3 × 4 ____ 4 × 3

g   3 + 4 ____ 4 × 2   h   (5 – 2) ____ (7 – 3)

i   (6 × 0) ____ (6 × 1)   j   5 × 6 ____ 3 × 5

k   (3 × 3) ____ 3 + 3   l   3 × 6 ____ (3 × 4)

m   (7 – 3) ____ (2 × 2)   n   (0 × 6) ____ (5 – 4)

o   (5 × 3) ____ (6 + 6)   p   (8 – 6) ____ (4 × 2)

Solve this riddle.
I am twice the product of 2 and 3. What number am I?

Sentences using *n*

If $n = 6$, find the value of $n + n$.
$n = 6$ is the **known fact**. $n + n$ is the **unknown**. Use the known fact to help you find the unknown fact.

$n + n$ or: $n + n = 2n$
$= 6 + 6$ $2n = 2 \times 6$
$= 12$ $= 12$

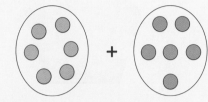

If $n = 20$, find the value of $30 - n$.
$30 - 20 = 10$
So $30 - n = 10$

If $10 + n = 13$, find the value of *n*.
$10 + n = 13$
$n = 13 - 10$
$n = 3$

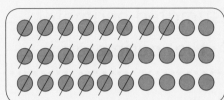

$10 \quad + \quad n \quad = \quad 13$

1   Solve the following. Use the method you find easiest.

a   If $n = 3$, find $n + n + n$.   b   If $n = 4$, find $n + n + n$.

_____   _____

c   If $n = 5$, find $n + n$.   d   If $n = 6$, find $n + n$.

_____   _____

e   If $n = 10$, find $20 - n$.   f   If $n = 5$, find $12 - n$.

_____   _____

g   If $n = 6$, find $15 + n$.   h   If $n = 9$, find $20 - n$.

_____   _____

i   If $n = 12$, find $24 - n$.   j   If $n = 8$, find $n + 12$

_____   _____

How much have you learned?

1 Estimate the perimeter of these shapes. Then measure using string and a ruler.

a

b

Estimated perimeter: ___

Actual perimeter: ___

Estimated perimeter: ___

Actual perimeter: ___

2 Find n.

a $5 + n = 15$ $n =$ ___   b $n = 13 + 10$ $n =$ ___

c $8 + n = 13$ $n =$ ___   d $15 + 5 = n$ $n =$ ___

e $n + 10 = 16$ $n =$ ___   f $12 + 12 = n$ $n =$ ___

g $n + 7 = 14$ $n =$ ___   h $6 + 8 = n$ $n =$ ___

3 Write an equivalent fraction for each diagram.

a
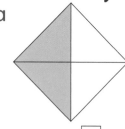

b
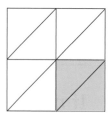

c
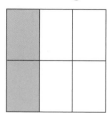

d
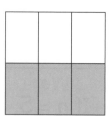

$\frac{1}{2} = \frac{\square}{4}$

$\frac{1}{\square} = \frac{2}{8}$

$\frac{1}{3} = \frac{2}{\square}$

$\frac{3}{6} = \frac{1}{\square}$

4 Circle the unit fractions in red. Circle the mixed numbers in blue. Circle the improper fractions in green.

$\frac{1}{5}$ $\frac{2}{7}$ $\frac{1}{9}$ $1\frac{3}{6}$ $\frac{8}{7}$ $1\frac{1}{2}$ $\frac{14}{4}$ $4\frac{2}{9}$ $\frac{1}{2}$ $\frac{1}{5}$ $\frac{10}{9}$

5 Colour to show:

a $\frac{1}{2}$ dozen

b I dozen

c $\frac{1}{4}$ dozen

How much have you learned?

6 Round off to the nearest ten.

    a   92 mangoes is about ____ mangoes.

    b   77 guineps is about ____ guineps.

    c   53 melons is about ____ melons.

    d   45 brooms is about ____ brooms.

7 **Jenny's patty sales**

		= 5 patties
Monday	🥐 🥐 🥐 🥐 🥐	
Tuesday	🥐 🥐 🥐 🥐	
Wednesday	🥐 🥐 🥐 🥐	
Thursday	🥐 🥐 🥐	
Friday	🥐 🥐	

    a   _____ patties were sold on Friday.

    b   Jenny sold the same number of patties on _____
        and _____.

    c   On Friday, Jenny sold ____ fewer patties than on
        Wednesday.

8 Fill in < or > to make each number sentence true.

    a (5×2) ___ $(3 + 8)$ b $(6 - 4)$ ___ $6 + 4$ c   \$250 ___ \$340

    d $\frac{1}{4}$ ___ $\frac{1}{2}$ e $\frac{3}{6}$ ___ $\frac{3}{4}$ f   5 g ___ 5 kg

    g   1 litre ___ 1 millilitre

9 Arrange each set of fractions in order from smallest to greatest.

    a $\frac{1}{3}$ $\frac{1}{4}$ $\frac{1}{2}$ _____   b $\frac{2}{3}$ $\frac{1}{3}$ $\frac{3}{3}$ _____

    c $\frac{2}{4}$ $\frac{1}{4}$ $\frac{4}{4}$ _____   d $\frac{1}{4}$ $\frac{1}{3}$ $\frac{3}{4}$ $\frac{1}{2}$ _____

    e $\frac{2}{3}$ $\frac{2}{4}$ $\frac{1}{3}$ $\frac{3}{4}$ _____   f $\frac{3}{4}$ $\frac{1}{2}$ $\frac{2}{3}$ $\frac{1}{3}$ _____

Unit 13 More sentences using n

$$12 - 7 = n$$
$$12 - 7 = 5 \quad \text{or:} \quad 7 + 5 = 12$$
$$n = 5 \qquad\qquad\quad n = 5$$

1 Use addition to help you solve these subtraction problems.

a $16 - 9 = n$

$9 + \underline{\quad} = 16$

$n = \underline{\quad}$

b $12 - 3 = n$

$3 + \underline{\quad} = 12$

$n = \underline{\quad}$

c $18 - 10 = n$

$\underline{\quad} + \underline{\quad} = \underline{\quad}$

$n = \underline{\quad}$

d $15 - 6 = n$

$\underline{\quad} + \underline{\quad} = \underline{\quad}$

$n = \underline{\quad}$

e $14 - 9 = n$

$\underline{\quad} + \underline{\quad} = \underline{\quad}$

$n = \underline{\quad}$

f $13 - 4 = n$

$\underline{\quad} + \underline{\quad} = \underline{\quad}$

$n = \underline{\quad}$

2 Draw dots to help you find the value of n in each number sentence.

a $8 + 7 = n$

b $5 + n = 15$

c $3 \times n = 21$

d $10 + 7 = n$

e $3 \times 5 = n$

f $11 + n = 16$

Solve this riddle.
My tens digit is three times my ones digit. My digits add up to four. What number am I?

Problem-solving

1   Decide whether you need to add, subtract, multiply or divide.
    Then write each number sentence and solve the problem.

   a   4 boys received 2 pencils each. How many pencils did
       they get altogether?

   _____

   b   The sum of 9, 3 and 2 is _____.

   c   What number divided by 4 gives 3?

   _____

   d   I buy an apple for $25. I pay with two $20 coins. I get

       _____ change.

   e   What is the difference between $10 and $18?

   _____

   f   10 children each pay $20 to ride the bounce-about.

       They pay _____ altogether.

2   Solve these problems mentally (without writing out the sum).
   a   Bill picks 12 mangoes. He finds 6 more. He has ____
       mangoes altogether.

   b   Fred gets a box of 30 cookies. He eats 15. ____ are left.

   c   In a class of 40 students, 23 bought patties. ____ did not
       buy patties.

3   Make up a word problem for each number sentence. Write it
    in your exercise book and solve it.
   a   30 − 16   b   23 + 15   c   5 × 3

Subtraction pictures

1 a Work out each problem.
   b Colour the shapes that have answers higher than **200**.
   c What picture do you see?

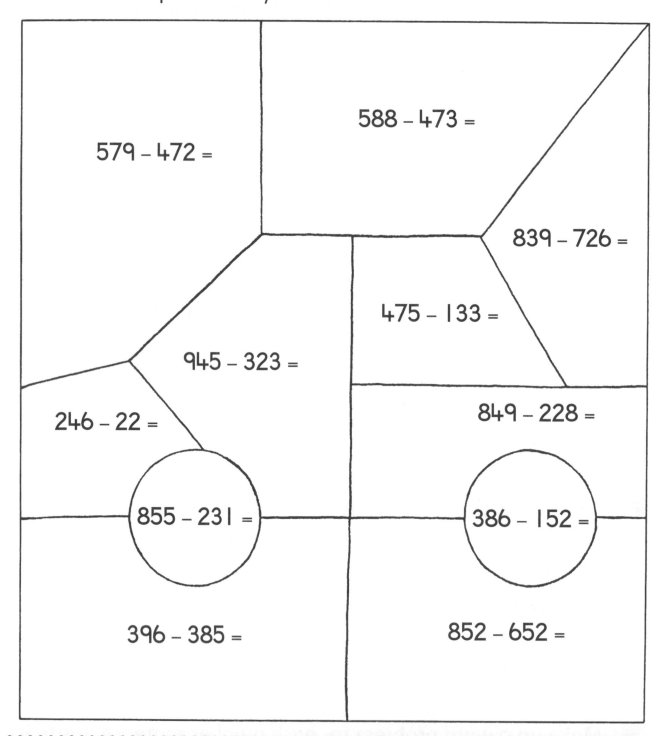

579 – 472 =

588 – 473 =

839 – 726 =

475 – 133 =

945 – 323 =

246 – 22 =

849 – 228 =

855 – 231 =

386 – 152 =

396 – 385 =

852 – 652 =

Make up your own subtraction problem about going shopping. Exchange problems with a friend. Work out your friend's problem in your exercise book.

Unit 14 Working with lengths

100 centimetres (cm) = 1 metre (m)
1 000 metres (m) = 1 kilometre (km)

1 Which unit would you use to measure these lengths:
cm, m or km?

a
finger

_____

b
garden hose

_____

c
house

_____

d
a pencil

_____

e
the distance a car
drives in an hour

_____

f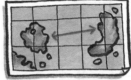
the distance
between 2 islands

_____

2 Estimate the total length. Then calculate the answer.

a 15 km + 13 km   b 27 m + 22 m   c 15 cm + 28 cm

Estimate: _____   _____   _____

Answer: _____   _____   _____

d 39 km – 13 km   e 32 m – 15 m   f 20 cm – 11 cm

Estimate: _____   _____   _____

Answer: _____   _____   _____

3 What is the difference between 20 km and 12 km? _____

4 A fence is 25 m long. I make it 10 m longer.
What is the new length? _____

5 The puppy is 38 cm long and the kitten is 30 cm long.
How much longer is the puppy than the kitten? _____

6 The width of a page is 20 cm and the length is 30 cm.
Calculate the perimeter of the page. _____

Estimating perimeter

1 Work in groups.

   a   Estimate the perimeter of each object or place.
Write your estimate in the table.

   b   Measure using string, metre rules and tape measures.
Write your measurements in the table.

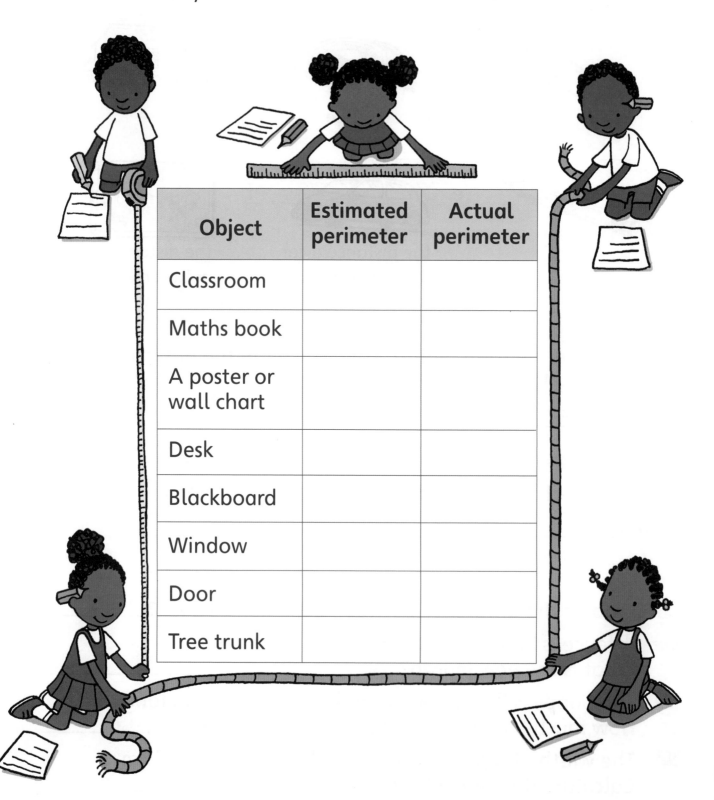

Object	Estimated perimeter	Actual perimeter
Classroom		
Maths book		
A poster or wall chart		
Desk		
Blackboard		
Window		
Door		
Tree trunk		

Metres and centimetres

 1 a Work in pairs. Measure each other's heights.
Record your height in the table in two ways.
For example, 135 cm is also 1 m 35 cm.

b Collect results from other pairs and record these in
the table.

Name	Height in cm	Height in m	Previous measured height	Have I grown?

3 Draw a graph to show the information. Who is the tallest?

 Why do you think we use tables and graphs to show
information? How do tables and graphs help us?

Measurement

1 Match each object to the correct unit of measurement.

Object	Unit of measurement
	litre kilogram metre centimetre

2 Write the best unit for measuring each of these objects.

a _____

b _____

c _____

d _____

e _____

f _____

g _____

h _____

Unit 15 Fractions

$\frac{1}{2}$ of the circle is blue.

$\frac{1}{2} + \frac{1}{2}$ = a whole circle.

$\frac{1}{2} + \frac{1}{2}$ = 1

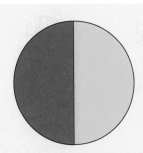

$\frac{1}{2}$ of the circle is yellow.

$\frac{3}{4}$ of the circle is blue.

$\frac{1}{4} + \frac{1}{4} + \frac{1}{4} = \frac{3}{4}$

$\frac{1}{4} + \frac{1}{4} + \frac{1}{4} + \frac{1}{4}$ = 1

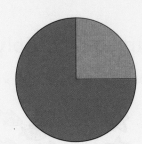

$\frac{1}{4}$ of the circle is grey.

1 Fill in the correct fractions.

a ___ of the circle is red. ___ of the circle is blue.

b ___ of the square is orange. ___ of the square is red. ___ of the square is blue.

c ___ of the square is yellow. ___ of the square is purple.

d ___ of the triangle is red. ___ of the triangle is yellow.

e ___ of the circle is red. ___ of the circle is blue. ___ is orange.

2 Use the pictures to help you work out these sums.

a  $\frac{1}{2}$ + ___ = 1

b  ___ + ___ + ___ + ___ = 1

c 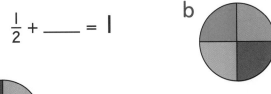 ___ + ___ + ___ = 1

d 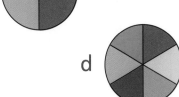 ___ + ___ + ___ + ___ + ___ + ___ = 1

Multiplying

$2 \times 4 = 8$
2 groups of 4 equal 8.

$4 \times 2 = 8$
4 groups of 2 equal 8.

1 Circle the groups to help you multiply.

a $2 \times 3 = \underline{\hspace{1cm}}$ $3 \times 2 = \underline{\hspace{1cm}}$ | b $2 \times 5 = \underline{\hspace{1cm}}$ $5 \times 2 = \underline{\hspace{1cm}}$

c $4 \times 3 = \underline{\hspace{1cm}}$ $2 \times 6 = \underline{\hspace{1cm}}$ | d $3 \times 4 = \underline{\hspace{1cm}}$ $6 \times 2 = \underline{\hspace{1cm}}$

e $1 \times 5 = \underline{\hspace{1cm}}$ $5 \times 1 = \underline{\hspace{1cm}}$ | f $3 \times 5 = \underline{\hspace{1cm}}$ $5 \times 3 = \underline{\hspace{1cm}}$

2 Draw dots or shapes to help you multiply.

a $1 \times 6 = \underline{\hspace{0.6cm}}$	b $4 \times 5 = \underline{\hspace{0.6cm}}$	c $6 \times 1 = \underline{\hspace{0.6cm}}$	d $5 \times 4 = \underline{\hspace{0.6cm}}$
e $2 \times 7 = \underline{\hspace{0.6cm}}$	f $3 \times 6 = \underline{\hspace{0.6cm}}$	g $7 \times 2 = \underline{\hspace{0.6cm}}$	h $6 \times 3 = \underline{\hspace{0.6cm}}$
i $5 \times 6 = \underline{\hspace{0.6cm}}$	j $3 \times 7 = \underline{\hspace{0.6cm}}$	k $6 \times 5 = \underline{\hspace{0.6cm}}$	l $7 \times 3 = \underline{\hspace{0.6cm}}$

More multiplying

$3 \times 2 =$ ___

3 groups with 2 objects in each group

$3 \times 2 = 6$

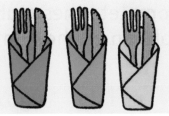

1 Find the answers. Draw pictures to help you.

a $3 \times 4 =$ ___

b $2 \times 4 =$ ___

c $2 \times 5 =$ ___

d $5 \times 3 =$ ___

e $2 \times 10 =$ ___

f $5 \times 1 =$ ___

g $2 \times 6 =$ ___

h $10 \times 1 =$ ___

i $2 \times 2 =$ ___

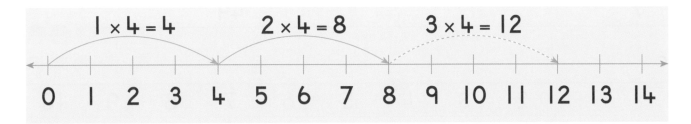

2 Draw arrows on the number lines to work out these multiplication sums.

a $3 \times 5 =$ ___

b $4 \times 3 =$ ___

c $2 \times 7 =$ ___

Multiplication facts

1 Complete these tables. Multiply the number at the top of the column by the number at the beginning of each row.

a

×	1	2	3	4	5	6	7	8	9	10
2	2	4								
3										
4					20	24				

b

×	1	2	3	4	5	6	7	8	9	10
5					25			40	45	
6						36				60
7							49			

c

×	1	2	3	4	5	6	7	8	9	10
8		16						64		
9									81	
10										100

2 Use the tables above to help you solve these multiplication sentences.

a $7 \times 3 = $ ___ b $3 \times 9 = $ ___ c $5 \times 4 = $ ___

$3 \times 7 = $ ___ $9 \times 3 = $ ___ $4 \times 5 = $ ___

d $3 \times 10 = $ ___ e $2 \times 9 = $ ___ f $4 \times 7 = $ ___

$10 \times 3 = $ ___ $9 \times 2 = $ ___ $7 \times 4 = $ ___

Multiplying bigger numbers

There are many different ways to multiply bigger numbers. We can use columns to help us. Look at these examples.

57×3

hundreds	tens	ones
	$^{+2}5$	7
×		3
1	7	1

First multiply the ones.
$3 \times 7 = 21$
Carry 2 tens into the tens column.
Then multiply the tens.
$3 \times 5 = 15$ $\qquad$ $15 + 2 = 17$
Remember to add the carried tens to your answer for the tens column. The answer to a multiplication sum is called the **product**.

$25 \times 4 = (20 + 5) \times 4$

	20	5
× 4	80	20

$80 + 20 = 100$

$25 \times 15 = (20 + 5) \times (10 + 5)$

×	20	5
10	200	50
5	100	25

$$\begin{array}{r} 250 \\ + \ 125 \\ \hline 375 \end{array}$$

---

1 Find the products. Work in your exercise book.

a 72×4 $\qquad$ b 45×3 $\qquad$ c 16×12 $\qquad$ d 22×6

e 12×5 $\qquad$ f 13×16 $\qquad$ g 37×3 $\qquad$ h 44×14

2 Your teacher will give you some domino cards. Join each card to a card that has the same solution. For example:

2×4	3×2	6×1	2×2	4×1	3×6

Continue the pattern for **28** dominoes. Play in groups of **4**.

Multiplying by 0

Any number multiplied by 0 is 0.

 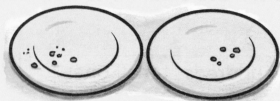

Each plate has 1 doughnut.
$2 \times 1 = 2$

Each plate has 0 doughnuts.
$2 \times 0 = 0$

1 Multiply.

a $4 \times 0 = $ ____

b $49 \times 0 = $ ____

c $0 \times 18 = $ ____

d $0 \times 7 = $ ____

e $8 \times 0 = $ ____

f $4 \times 0 = $ ____

g $68 \times 0 = $ ____

h $43 \times 0 = $ ____

i $0 \times 50 = $ ____

2 Draw sets to show these sums. The first one has been done for you as an example.

a 3×0

b 5×0

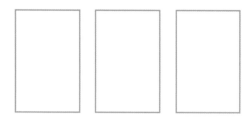

c 4×0

d 2×0

Operations

Find the sum means add. Find the product means multiply.
Find the difference means subtract the smaller number from the
bigger number.

Lollies Thank You! Gum

Hearts | Chocolate Stars | Chocolate nuts | mints | Chocolate Strawberries | White Drops

1 Count the chocolates. Fill in the amounts.

Chocolate stars ___   Mints ___   Chocolate nuts ___

Hearts ___   Chocolate strawberries ___   White drops ___

2 Write the answer. Then draw the kind of chocolate that
matches the answer. The first one has been done for you.

a	b	c
Product of 6 and 8 = 48	Sum of 21 and 26 = ___	Product of 3 and 10 = ___
d	**e**	**f**
Sum of 9 and 9 = ___	Product of 7 and 7 = ___	Sum of 28 and 8 = ___

January 2005						
Sunday	Monday	Tuesday	Wednesday	Thursday	Friday	Saturday
						1
2	3	4	5	6	7	8
9	10	11	12	13	14	15
16	17	18	19	20	21	22
23	24	25	26	27	28	29
30	31					

1 Peter, Mark, Sandy and Rita all celebrated their birthdays on 15 January 2005. Use the table below to work out their ages on that day.

Name	Born on	Age in years
Peter	15 January 1994	
Mark	15 January 1995	
Sandy	15 January 1996	
Rita	15 January 1998	

2 a Simon was 5 years old on 4 January this year.
How old will he be in 2 years' time? ____

b Robert's birthday is on the same day as Simon's, but he is 3 years older. How old was Robert on 4 January this year? ____

c Sharon was born 2 years before Simon.
How old was Sharon on Simon's 5th birthday? ____

d Cathy is 2 years and 6 months older than Robert.
How old will she be when Robert is 8 years old? ____

Unit 18 Temperature

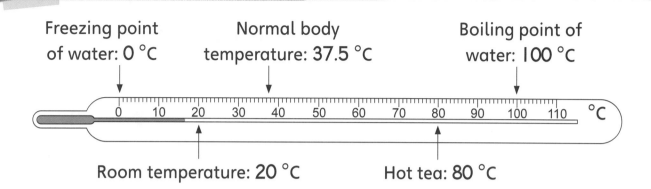

Freezing point of water: 0 °C
Normal body temperature: 37.5 °C
Boiling point of water: 100 °C

Room temperature: 20 °C
Hot tea: 80 °C

1 Circle the temperature that matches each situation most closely.

a Cold day
65 °C
18 °C
80 °C

b Hot soup
40 °C
80 °C
20 °C

c Hot summer day
30 °C
12 °C
100 °C

d Classroom
4 °C
60 °C
20 °C

e Ice cube
0 °C
20 °C
35 °C

f Person with fever
39 °C
37.5 °C
50 °C

2 Write the temperature shown on each thermometer.

a   b   c   d   e

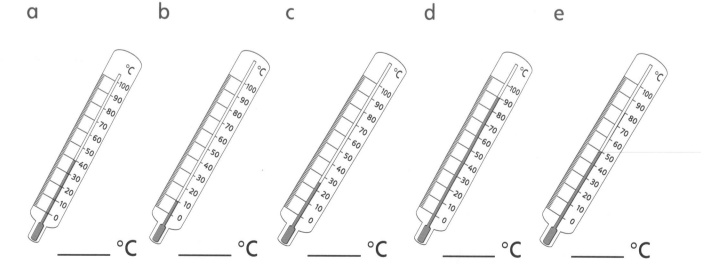

_____ °C   _____ °C   _____ °C   _____ °C   _____ °C

Adding and multiplying

1 Fill in the missing numbers in each number sentence.

a

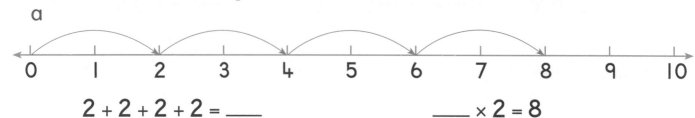

$2 + 2 + 2 + 2 =$ ____   ____ $\times 2 = 8$

Four groups of two = ____

b

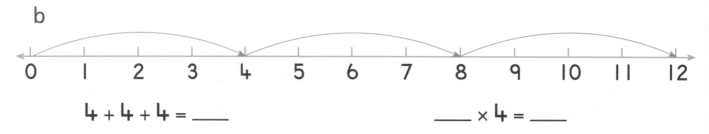

$4 + 4 + 4 =$ ____   ____ $\times 4 =$ ____

Three groups of four = ____

c

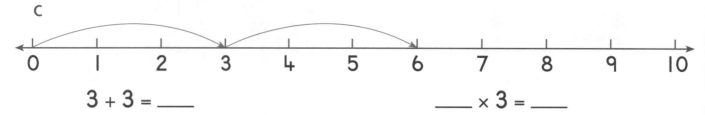

$3 + 3 =$ ____   ____ $\times 3 =$ ____

Two groups of three = ____

d

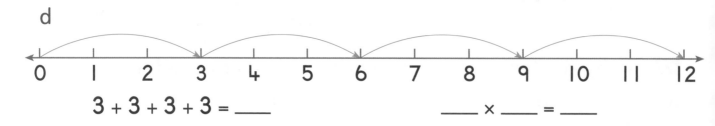

$3 + 3 + 3 + 3 =$ ____   ____ $\times$ ____ $=$ ____

Four groups of three = ____

e

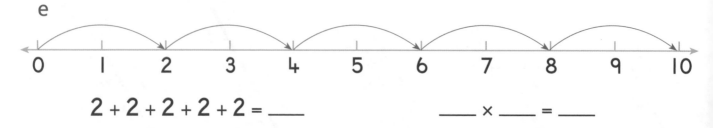

$2 + 2 + 2 + 2 + 2 =$ ____   ____ $\times$ ____ $=$ ____

Five groups of two = ____

Multiplying

Each plate has 4 cookies.
2 sets of 4 = 8
2 × 4 = 8

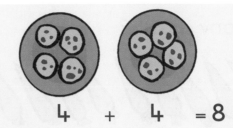

4 + 4 = 8

1 Complete these number sentences:

2 sets of 3 = 6

2 × 3 = 6

2 sets of ___ = ___

2 × ___ = ___

___ sets of 3 = ___

___ × ___ = ___

___ sets of ___ = ___

___ × ___ = ___

___ sets of ___ = ___

___ × ___ = ___

___ sets of ___ = ___

___ × ___ = ___

2 Draw the sets. Then write the answer.

4 × 2 = ___   2 × 5 = ___   2 × 6 = ___   1 × 4 = ___

3 Nina uses 6 buckets of sand to make one sandcastle.
She builds 3 sandcastles.

___ × ___ = ___ She uses ___ buckets of sand.

4 Each sandcastle has 4 flags. Jim builds 3 sandcastles.
___ × ___ = ___ He uses ___ flags.

5 2 of the sandcastles have moats around them. Nina uses
5 buckets of water to fill each moat.

___ × ___ = ___ She uses ___ buckets of water.

Multiplying by 3

How many carrots?

3 + 3 + 3 + 3 + 3 = 15
We can also say 'five sets of three' or 5 × 3.
5 + 5 + 5 = 15
Or we can say: 'three sets of five' or 3 × 5.
5 × 3 = 3 × 5 = 15
5 and 3 are the **factors**. 15 is the **product**.

1 Multiply.

a

3 × 7 = ____

Factors: ____ and ____.

Product: ____

7 × 3 = ____

b

3 × ____ = ____

Factors: ____ and ____.

Product: ____

____ × ____ = ____

c

3 × ____ = ____

Factors: ____ and ____.

Product: ____

____ × ____ = ____

d

3 × ____ = ____

Factors: ____ and ____.

Product: ____

____ × ____ = ____

2 Complete this table.

3 ×	1	2	3	4	5	6	7	8	9	10
Product	3				15					

Multiplication game

1 Your teacher will give you some domino cards. Join each card to a card that has the same solution.

| 2 × 4 | 3 × 2 | 6 × 1 | 2 × 2 | 4 × 1 | 3 × 6 |

$$3 \times 2 = 6 \qquad 2 \times 2 = 4$$
$$6 \times 1 = 6 \qquad 4 \times 1 = 4$$

Continue the pattern for **28** dominoes. Play in groups of **4**.

2 Now make up your own multiplication sentences to fill in this domino line.

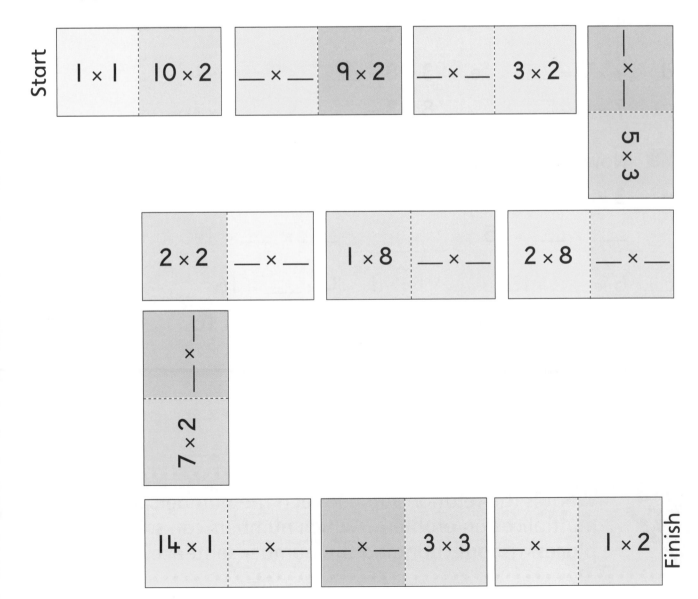

Multiplying

$5 \times 2 =$ ___
Here is another way to multiply.
Use the number line.

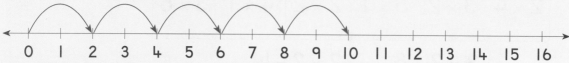

Start at 0. Move forward 2 places. Do this 5 times.
5 times 2 equals 10.
$5 \times 2 = 10$

1 Use the long number line to help you multiply.

a $6 \times 4 =$ ___   b $5 \times 5 =$ ___   c $2 \times 10 =$ ___
  $4 \times 6 =$ ___ $5 \times 5 =$ ___ $10 \times 2 =$ ___

d $4 \times 7 =$ ___   e $3 \times 8 =$ ___   f $6 \times 4 =$ ___
  $7 \times 4 =$ ___ $8 \times 3 =$ ___ $4 \times 6 =$ ___

2 Now use the number line to help you complete these.

a $3 \times$ ___ $= 15$ b $2 \times$ ___ $= 14$
  ___ $\times$ ___ $= 15$ ___ $\times$ ___ $= 14$

c $6 \times$ ___ $= 18$ d $4 \times$ ___ $= 16$
  ___ $\times$ ___ $= 18$ ___ $\times$ ___ $= 16$

3 Now make up two examples of your own.

a ___ $\times$ ___ $=$ ___   b ___ $\times$ ___ $=$ ___
  ___ $\times$ ___ $=$ ___   ___ $\times$ ___ $=$ ___

What is the relationship between the numbers in a multiplication problem? Which numbers can switch places without changing the number sentence?

0 1 2 3 4 5 6 7 8 9 10 11 12 13 14 15 16 17 18 19 20 21 22 23 24 25 26 27 28 29 30

Multiplying by 10

1 group of 10
1 × 10 = 10

10 + 10 + 10 = 30
3 × 10 = 30

What pattern do you notice in the products?

1   Work out these by adding and multiplying.

a   10

     1 × 10 = ___

b   10 + 10 = ___

     2 × 10 = ___

2   Now work out these.

a   10 + 10 + 10 = ___

     ___ × 10 = ___

b   10 + 10 + 10 + 10 + 10 = ___

     ___ × ___ = ___

3   Draw groups to help you work out these. Use tens.

a   7 × 10 = ___   b   8 × 10 = ___

c   ___ × 10 = 90   d   ___ × ___ = 100

Dividing by 1 or 0

When you divide, the number you are dividing is called the **dividend**. The number you divide by is called the **divisor**. The answer of the division sentence is called the **quotient**.

8 ÷ 4 = 2
8 is the dividend.
4 is the divisor.
2 is the quotient.

1 and 0 are special numbers in division.
If the divisor is 1, the quotient is equal to the dividend: 5 ÷ 1 = 5
If the divisor and the dividend are the same, the quotient is 1: 4 ÷ 4 = 1

6 ÷ 1 = 6
6 ÷ 6 = 1

If the dividend is 0, the quotient is 0: 0 ÷ 4 = 0

Try dividing a number by 0 on your calculator. What happens? Why do you think this is?

---

1 a   3 ÷ 1 = _____   b   8 ÷ 1 = _____

   c   10 ÷ 1 = _____   d   100 ÷ 1 = _____

   e $\frac{1}{2}$ ÷ 1 = _____   f   9 ÷ 1 = _____

2 a   12 ÷ 12 = _____   b   45 ÷ 45 = _____

   c   11 ÷ 11 = _____   d   4 ÷ 4 = _____

   e   7 ÷ 7 = _____   f   18 ÷ 18 = _____

Multiplication: $7 \times 1 = 1 \times 7$

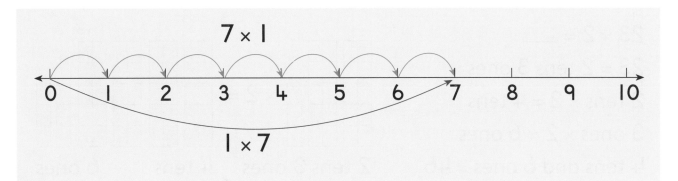

1 Draw the hops and complete the number sentences.

a
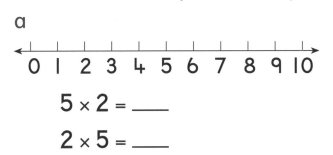

$5 \times 2 = \underline{}$

$2 \times 5 = \underline{}$

b
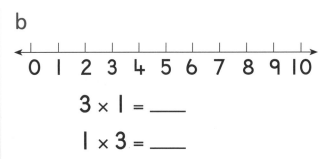

$3 \times 1 = \underline{}$

$1 \times 3 = \underline{}$

c
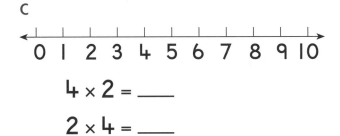

$4 \times 2 = \underline{}$

$2 \times 4 = \underline{}$

d
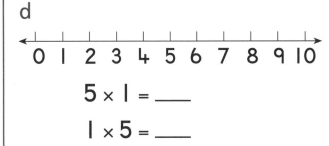

$5 \times 1 = \underline{}$

$1 \times 5 = \underline{}$

e
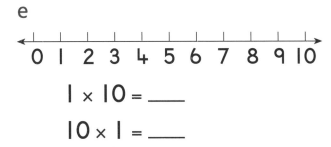

$1 \times 10 = \underline{}$

$10 \times 1 = \underline{}$

f
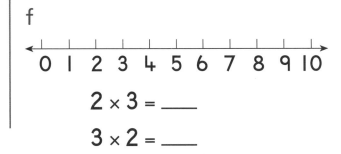

$2 \times 3 = \underline{}$

$3 \times 2 = \underline{}$

2 Complete these.

a $\quad 3 \times 4 = 4 \times \underline{}$

b $\quad 5 \times 2 = 2 \times \underline{}$

c $\quad 2 \times 6 = \underline{} \times 2$

d $\quad 2 \times \underline{} = 4 \times 2$

e $\quad \underline{} \times 5 = 5 \times 1$

f $\quad 2 \times \underline{} = 1 \times 2$

g $\quad 2 \times \underline{} = 3 \times 2$

h $\quad 1 \times \underline{} = 3 \times 1$

Multiplying 2-digit numbers

23 × 2 = ___
23 = 2 tens 3 ones
2 tens × 2 = 4 tens
3 ones × 2 = 6 ones
4 tens and 6 ones = 46
23 × 2 = 46

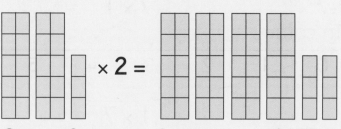

2 tens 3 ones   4 tens   6 ones

×2   ×2

Here are two more ways to work it out.

In columns:

tens	ones
2	3
×	2
4	6

Using expanded notation:

23   = (20 + 3)
23 × 2 = (20 × 2) + (3 × 2)
            = 40 + 6
            = 46

1 Multiply in columns.

a   30
      × 3
      ____

b   42
      × 2
      ____

c   21
      × 3
      ____

d   24
      × 2
      ____

e   12
      × 4
      ____

f   11
      × 5
      ____

2 Multiply using expanded notation.

a   41 × 3   b   22 × 4   c   32 × 3

Multiplying and regrouping

$47 \times 2 = $ ____

In columns:

$$^{+1}47$$
$$\underline{\times\ 2}$$
$$94$$

$7 \times 2 = 14$ (1 ten 4 ones)
Write 4 in the ones column.
Carry 1 to the tens column.

$4 \times 2 = 8$. Add the 1 you carried.
$8 + 1 = 9$
$47 \times 2 = 94$

In expanded notation:

$$47 \qquad = 40 + 7$$
$$47 \times 2 = (40 \times 2) + (7 \times 2)$$
$$\qquad\quad = 80 + 14$$
$$\qquad\quad = 94$$

1 Multiply in columns.

a
$$18$$
$$\underline{\times\ 3}$$

b
$$27$$
$$\underline{\times\ 2}$$

c
$$16$$
$$\underline{\times\ 3}$$

d
$$29$$
$$\underline{\times\ 2}$$

e
$$17$$
$$\underline{\times\ 4}$$

f
$$38$$
$$\underline{\times\ 2}$$

2 Multiply using expanded notation.

a 36×2 b 25×3 c 19×4

Multiplying bigger numbers

$123 \times 2 = \underline{}$

Just as before, you can use columns or expanded notation.

In columns:

$$\begin{array}{r} 123 \\ \times\ 2 \\ \hline 246 \end{array}$$

In expanded notation:

$123 = 100 + 20 + 3$
$123 \times 2 = (100 \times 2) + (20 \times 2) + (3 \times 2)$
$= 200 + 40 + 6$
$= 246$
$123 \times 2 = 246$

Here is another example.

157×2

In columns:

$$\begin{array}{r} {}^{+1}1\overset{1}{5}7 \\ \times\ 2 \\ \hline 314 \end{array}$$

In expanded notation:

$157 = 100 + 50 + 7$
$= (100 \times 2) + (50 \times 2) + (7 \times 2)$
$= 200 + 100 + 14$
$= 314$
$157 \times 2 = 314$

1 Multiply in columns without regrouping.

a
$$\begin{array}{r} 142 \\ \times\ 2 \\ \hline \end{array}$$

b
$$\begin{array}{r} 234 \\ \times\ 2 \\ \hline \end{array}$$

c
$$\begin{array}{r} 121 \\ \times\ 4 \\ \hline \end{array}$$

2 Multiply in columns. Regroup where needed. Use expanded notation to help you check your answers.

a
$$\begin{array}{r} 257 \\ \times\ 3 \\ \hline \end{array}$$

b
$$\begin{array}{r} 198 \\ \times\ 4 \\ \hline \end{array}$$

c
$$\begin{array}{r} 142 \\ \times\ 2 \\ \hline \end{array}$$

d
$$\begin{array}{r} 127 \\ \times\ 3 \\ \hline \end{array}$$

e
$$\begin{array}{r} 268 \\ \times\ 3 \\ \hline \end{array}$$

f
$$\begin{array}{r} 193 \\ \times\ 4 \\ \hline \end{array}$$

Estimating products

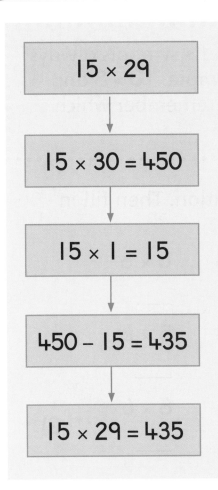

It can be easier to multiply using rounded numbers.
Round off 29 to 30.

Multiply 15 by 30.

You added one set of 15 to round off.

Subtract it from 450.

1 Use rounding off to help you multiply. Check your answers using a calculator.

a   24 × 19

b   13 × 19

c   22 × 29

d   18 × 9

e   18 × 29

f   16 × 19

Comparing products

Remember, the open side of the < and > symbols always points to the bigger number. For example, 10 > 8 and 7 < 8. Can you think of a fun way to remember which way the signs point?

1 Write the product under each multiplication. Then fill in < or > to show which product is greater.

a 6 × 3   5 × 4   b 5 × 3   6 × 6

___   ___   ___   ___

c 8 × 3   5 × 7   d 5 × 8   5 × 6

___   ___   ___   ___

e 4 × 8   5 × 5   f 7 × 4   6 × 6

___   ___   ___   ___

2 Write < or > to show which product is greater. You can use your calculator to help you check your answers.

a 7 × 6 ___ 6 × 5   b 6 × 7 ___ 7 × 8

c 5 × 5 ___ 6 × 7   d 4 × 9 ___ 5 × 8

e 7 × 3 ___ 5 × 5   f 5 × 6 ___ 3 × 8

g 5 × 3 ___ 4 × 7   h 5 × 4 ___ 2 × 6

i 8 × 3 ___ 2 × 7   j 8 × 3 ___ 5 × 6

k 9 × 3 ___ 6 × 4   l 5 × 7 ___ 6 × 6

3 Write your own multiplication sums to make each sentence true.

a 2 × 7 > _____   b 8 × 3 < _____

c 5 × 5 < _____   d 7 × 5 > _____

e 4 × 6 > _____   f 4 × 8 < _____

Looking back

1 Find the product. Draw pictures to show your working.

a $3 + 3 + 3 + 3$ b $4 + 4 + 4$ c $5 + 5$

___ × 3 = ___   ___ × 4 = ___   ___ × 5 = ___

d $4 × 2 =$ ___   e $3 × 5 =$ ___   f $4 × 4 =$ ___

2 Find *n*.

a $5 + 5 = n$ b $n + 8 = 16$ c $n + 9 = 18$

n = ___   *n* = ___   *n* = ___

d $n - 10 = 5$ e $n - 12 = 12$ f $18 - n = 12$

n = ___   *n* = ___   *n* = ___

3 Find the product. Then write a matching division sum using the same numbers.

a $8 × 3 =$ ___   b $7 × 3 =$ ___   c $5 × 4 =$ ___

___ ÷ ___ = ___   ___ ÷ ___ = ___   ___ ÷ ___ = ___

4 True or false?

a   If you multiply a number by 0, the product is 1. _____

b   If you multiply a number by 0, the product is 0. _____

c   If you multiply a number by 1, the product is the factor you multiplied by 1. _____

5 Write the temperature shown on each thermometer.

a   b   c   d

___ °C   ___ °C   ___ °C   ___ °C

Looking back

6 Choose cm, m or km to complete each sentence below.

a   A front door is about 2 ____ high.

b   Your nose is about 3 ____ long.

c   The speed limit in town is about 30 ____ per hour.

d   The playing field is about 100 ____ long.

e   Your height is about 110 ____.

7 a   Jane was born on 15 May 1990. Her age on 15 May 2000 was _____.

b   Michael was born on 10 June 1994. His age on 10 June 2002 was _____.

c   Phyllis was born on 17 August 1999. She will be 12 years old on _____.

8 Write number sentences and solve.

a   Jolene cut two lengths of red ribbon from a roll. One piece was 15 cm long and the other piece was 12 cm long. What was the total length of ribbon that Jolene cut?

_____

b   Sandy built a sandcastle that was 25 cm high. Then she made it 10 cm taller. What was the new height of the sandcastle?

_____

c   A wall is 14 metres long. The builder adds another 21 metres to the wall. How long is the wall in total?

_____

9 Multiply using any method. Work in your exercise book.

a   128 × 2   b   437 × 2   c   328 × 2

_____   _____   _____

Open and closed figures

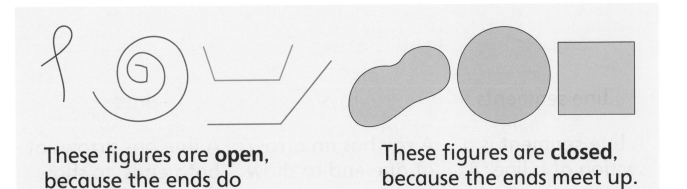

These figures are **open**, because the ends do not meet up.

These figures are **closed**, because the ends meet up.

1 Colour the closed figures in blue.
Circle the open figures in red.

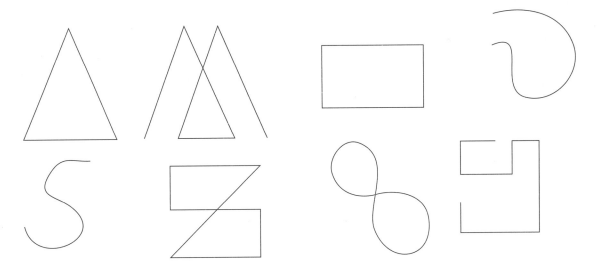

2 Design and draw four closed figures.

3 Design and draw four open figures.

Lines, rays and line segments

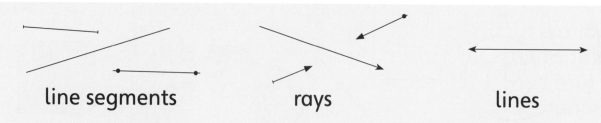

line segments	rays	lines

A **line segment** is a section of a line. A line segment has no arrows, because it is a piece of a line. It may have dots or lines to show its end points.

A **ray** has an arrow at one end to show that it has one end point but continues in one direction.

A **line** has arrows at both ends, to show that it continues in both directions.

1 Write the correct name for each figure.

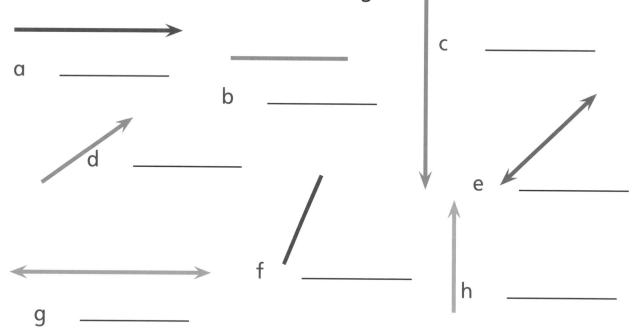

2 Draw a line.

3 Draw a line segment.

Rays, angles and square corners

Two rays that meet at their end points form an **angle**. The point where they meet is the **vertex**. The angle is the amount of turn between the rays. We measure angles in degrees (°).
A square corner measures $90°$.
For example, rays BA and BC meet at vertex B.
We can write the angle as $\angle CBA$ or $\angle B$ or $\hat{B}$.
Rays QP and QR meet at Q. $\angle PQR = 90°$

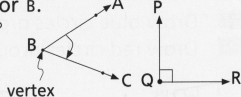

When you use three letters to name an angle, goes the letter that names the vertex in the middle.

1 Write the name of each angle.
Tick the right angles.

a

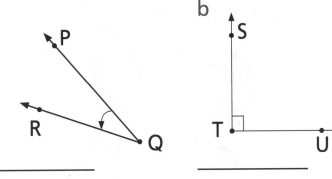

b

c

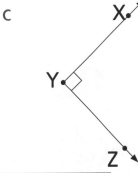

d

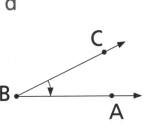

e

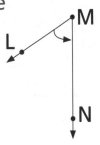

2 Draw sketches to show the following figures.

a line segment PQ

b rays AB and BC meeting at B

c right angle XYZ

Angles and right angles

The corner of a shape is called an angle.

angle

A triangle has three angles.

A right angle is a square corner.
Squares and rectangles have right angles.

right angle

A rectangle has four right angles.

1 Draw blue circles around any five angles.
2 Draw red circles around five right angles.

3 Draw three shapes that have right angles.

4 How many angles does each shape on the wall have?

Shape 1 ____   Shape 2 ____   Shape 3 ____

Shape 4 ____   Shape 5 ____

Simple closed paths

A polygon is a flat shape. Polygons are also called **plane shapes**, because we draw them on a plane (a flat area). Polygons have length and width, but not depth. You can also think of polygons as the **faces** of solid shapes. For example, a cube has six square faces. A polygon is a **simple closed path**. It is **simple** because it has straight sides, and it is **closed** because the sides all join up.

1. Here are some polygons. Match the names in the box with the polygons.

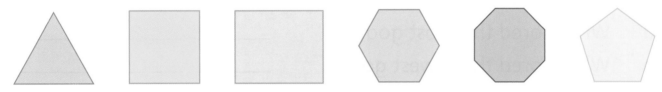

| hexagon | rectangle | pentagon | triangle | octagon | square |

2. Match each path description in the first column with the correct set of sketches in the second column. The first one has been done for you.

Path description	Sketches
open not simple	
open simple	
right-angled	
closed	
polygons	

Using tally marks

1 Roy kept a tally of the number of goals his friends scored in a soccer match.

Names	Goals	
	Tally	Number
Ryan	卌 卌 卌	15
Sue	卌 卌 I	11
Linda	卌 卌 卌 II	17

I = 1   卌 = 5

a Who scored the most goals? _____

b Who scored the fewest goals? _____

2 Write down the numbers that these tallies represent.

a 卌 III   b 卌 卌 II   c 卌 卌   d 卌 卌 III

_____   _____   _____   _____

3 When we add up tallies, we count in multiples of ____.

4 Draw tally marks for the following numbers.

Number	Tally
13	
20	
16	
4	
18	
22	
5	

Bar graphs

1 This bar graph shows the favourite colours of the pupils in a class.

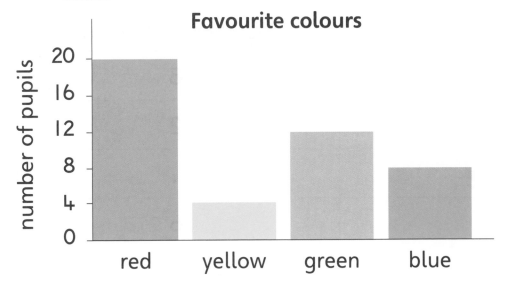

a   Which colour do the most pupils like?   _____

b   How many pupils like this colour?   _____

c   How many pupils like blue?   _____

d   Which colour do only 4 pupils like?   _____

e   How many more pupils like green than like blue?   _____

f   How many pupils are there in the class altogether?   _____

2 Look at this bar graph. Use it to complete the table.

T-shirt colours of children in the class

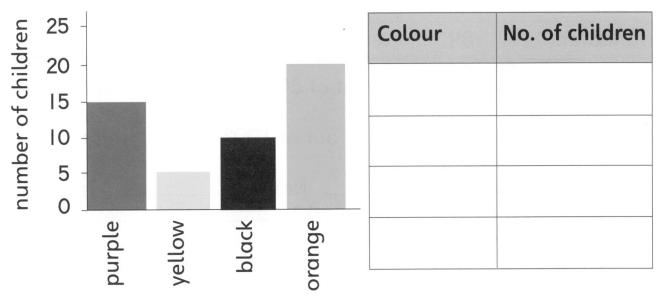

Colour	No. of children

Tables

1   This table shows what pupils in a class chose for lunch.
    Use the table to complete the statements below.

Lunch item	Number of children
Patty	8
Sandwich	12
Hamburger	4
Pizza	6

a   There are ___ children in the class altogether.
b   The most popular food was ___.
c   The least popular food was ___.
d   The fraction of the class that chose pizza was ___.
e   Write 3 more questions about the table and find the answers.

2   A class wrote three maths tests in one term. Each test was
    marked out of 100. At the end of the term, each student got
    a total mark out of 300. This table shows their marks.

Student	Test 1	Test 2	Test 3	Total
Janet	96	68	85	
Ava	95	62	74	
Damian	99	72	79	
Jonathan	89	62	86	

a   Work out the total mark out of 300 for each pupil and
    complete the table.
b   What was the highest mark out of 100? Who got this mark,
    and for which test?
    Highest mark out of 100: ___   Name: _____   Test: ___
c   Who got the highest total mark? _____
d   Who got the lowest total mark? _____
e   Write 3 more questions about the table and find the answers.

Interpreting pictographs

1. This pictograph shows how many mangoes Jenny picked in a week.

Mangoes picked	
Monday	🥭 🥭 🥭 🥭 🥭 🥭 🥭
Tuesday	🥭 🥭 🥭 🥭
Wednesday	🥭 🥭 🥭 🥭
Thursday	🥭 🥭 🥭 🥭 🥭
Friday	🥭 🥭 🥭 🥭 🥭 🥭

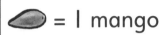 = 1 mango

Answer these questions using the pictograph.

a   On which day did Jenny pick the most mangoes? _____

b   On which days did she pick equal numbers of mangoes?

_____ and _____

c   How many mangoes did she pick altogether in the week? _____

d   How many more mangoes did she pick on Monday than on Wednesday? _____

2. This pictograph shows how many goldfish Jimmy's petshop sold in a week.

Goldfish sales at Jimmy's pet shop	
Monday	🐟 🐟 🐟
Tuesday	🐟
Wednesday	🐟 🐟
Thursday	🐟 🐟 🐟 🐟
Friday	🐟 🐟 🐟 🐟 🐟

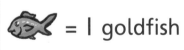 = 1 goldfish

Answer these questions using the pictograph.

a   How many goldfish were sold on Monday? _____

b   How many goldfish were sold on Wednesday? _____

c   How many more goldfish were sold on Friday than on Tuesday? _____

d   How many goldfish were sold altogether this week? _____

More pictographs

1 Melanie collected bottle tops for making earrings.

Bottle tops collected in a week	
Monday	🍪🍪
Tuesday	🍪🍪🍪🍪
Wednesday	🍪
Thursday	🍪🍪🍪
Friday	🍪🍪

 = 10 bottle tops

Answer these questions using the pictograph above.

a   Melanie collected the most bottle tops on _____.

b   Melanie collected the fewest bottle tops on _____.

c   How many bottle tops did Melanie collect altogether?   ____

d   On which day did Melanie collect double the number she collected the day before?   _____

e   What is the difference between the number of bottle tops she collected on Thursday and on Wednesday?   ____

 2 Find out the favourite ice-cream flavours of children in your class. Complete this pictograph. Don't forget the heading and the key.

Chocolate	
Vanilla	
Strawberry	
Mint	
Other	

Probability

1   Do these experiments and record your results.

a   Flip a 10c coin twenty times. Record the results below.

	Tally	Number
Heads		
Tails		

b   Collect results from five other pupils. Complete this table.

Name					
Heads					
Tails					

2   Use the second table to help you answer true or false.

a   The coin is more likely to land on heads than on tails.   ____

b   The coin is equally likely to land on heads and on tails.   ____

c   The coin is less likely to land on heads than on tails.   ____

3   Make a spinner like the one in the picture. Spin the arrow 24 times. Record your results below.

Arrow lands on	Tally	Number
Blue		
Red		
Yellow		

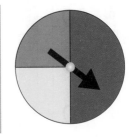

a   The arrow is most likely to land on _____.

b   The arrow is equally likely to land on _____ or _____.

4   Throw a dice 24 times. Record how many times each number comes up.

Side	⚀	⚁	⚂	⚃	⚄	⚅
Tally						
Number						

Collecting and recording data

1 St Rob is a small primary school in rural Jamaica. The school has six classes. A group of Grade 3 pupils counted the number of pupils in each class. They recorded their findings using tallies. Read the tallies and complete the table.

Class	Tally	Number of pupils
1A	|||| |||| |||| |||| |||| |||| ||||	
2A	|||| |||| |||| |||| |||| |||| |||| |||	
3A	|||| |||| |||| |||| |||| |||| |||| |||| ||||	
4A	|||| |||| |||| |||| |||| |||| |||| ||||	
5A	|||| |||| |||| |||| |||| |||| |||| |||| |||| ||||	
6A	|||| |||| |||| |||| |||| |||| |||| |||| ||||	

2 Look at the bar graph they drew to show the number of pupils.

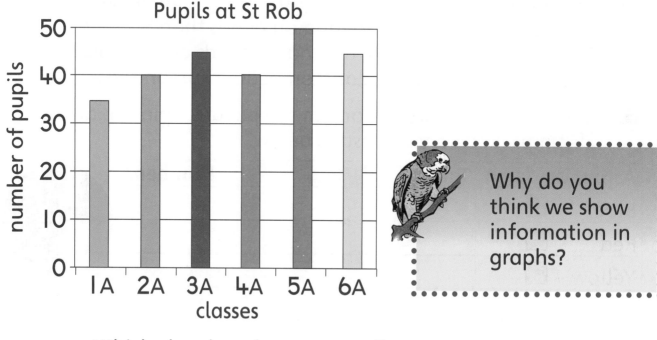

Pupils at St Rob

Why do you think we show information in graphs?

 a Which class has the most pupils? _____

 b Which classes have equal numbers of pupils? _____

 c Which class has more pupils, 5A or 6A? _____

3 Choose four classes in your school. Find out how many pupils are in each class. Collect your information using tallies. Draw a bar graph to show the results.

How much have you learned?

1
a $7 \times 6 = $ _____ b $9 \times 6 = $ _____ c $6 \times 6 = $ _____

$42 \div 6 = $ _____ $54 \div 6 = $ _____ $36 \div 6 = $ _____

d $12 \times 3 = $ _____ e $5 \times 4 = $ _____ f $5 \times 6 = $ _____

$36 \div 12 = $ _____ $20 \div 5 = $ _____ $30 \div 5 = $ _____

2
a $n \times 3 = 15$ b $n \times 7 = 42$ c $4 \times n = 16$

$n = $ _____ $n = $ _____ $n = $ _____

d $n \times 5 = 40$ e $8 \times n = 24$ f $n \times 3 = 24$

$n = $ _____ $n = $ _____ $n = $ _____

3 Fill in < or >.

a (5×3) _____ (6×2) b (7×3) _____ (5×4)

c (5×6) _____ (7×4) d (4×8) _____ (9×4)

e (6×7) _____ (8×5) f (4×6) _____ (6×5)

4 Write open or closed under each shape.

a 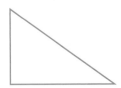 b c  d

_____ _____ _____ _____

e f g

_____ _____ _____

5 Multiply.

a $5 \times 10 = $ _____ b $6 \times 10 = $ _____ c $8 \times 10 = $ _____

d $\begin{array}{r} 144 \\ \times\ 2 \\ \hline \\ \end{array}$ e $\begin{array}{r} 203 \\ \times\ 4 \\ \hline \\ \end{array}$ f $\begin{array}{r} 103 \\ \times\ 5 \\ \hline \\ \end{array}$

How much have you learned?

6   Decide whether each figure is a: line segment, ray, line, right angle or angle.

a _____

b _____

c _____

d _____

e _____

f _____

g _____

h _____

i _____

j _____

....

7

a   What are the chances of landing on red compared with blue? For each spinner write **more likely**, **less likely** or **equally likely**.

b   Test your predictions using real spinners. Record your results in the table below.

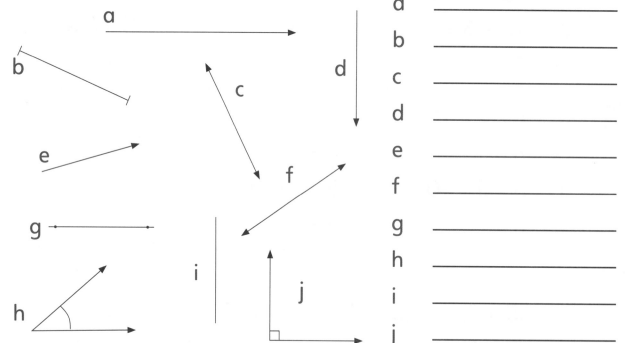

Probability of landing on red						
	Red	Blue	Red	Blue	Red	Blue
Tally						
Number						

True or false

1 Write **true** or **false** next to each number sentence. If the number sentence is false, write the true answer next to it.
For example:

8 × 100 = 800   True.
25 × 3 = 50   False.   25 × 3 = 75.

a   9 × 2 = 18   _____

b   20 ÷ 5 = 4   _____

c   15 ÷ 3 = 5   _____

d   13 − 6 = 7   _____

e   19 − 6 = 13   _____

f   22 − 10 = 2   _____

g   88 ÷ 2 = 44   _____

h   6 × 3 = 21   _____

i   12 + 3 = 15   _____

j   20 − 5 = 16   _____

k   17 + 4 = 21   _____

l   7 + 4 = 12   _____

Solve this riddle.
My tens digit is twice my ones digit.
Both digits add to make 12. What number am I?

Multiplying and dividing

1 Show on the number line how you work out these.

a

b $3 \times 3 = 9$ $9 \div 3 = 3$

```
  0  1  2  3  4  5  6  7  8  9  10 11 12 13 14 15 16 17 18 19 20
```

     $7 \times 2 =$ ___   ___ $\div 2 = 7$

c

```
  0  1  2  3  4  5  6  7  8  9  10 11 12 13 14 15 16 17 18 19 20
```

     $9 \times 2 =$ ___   ___ $\div$ ___ $=$ ___

d

```
  0  1  2  3  4  5  6  7  8  9  10 11 12 13 14 15 16 17 18 19 20
```

     $3 \times 5 =$ ___   ___ $\div$ ___ $=$ ___

e

```
  0  1  2  3  4  5  6  7  8  9  10 11 12 13 14 15 16 17 18 19 20 21 22 23 24 25
```

f $4 \times$ ___ $= 24$ $24 \div$ ___ $= 4$

```
  0  1  2  3  4  5  6  7  8  9  10 11 12 13 14 15 16 17 18 19 20
```

     $4 \times$ ___ $= 20$ $20 \div$ ___ $= 4$

2 Fill in +, −, × or ÷.

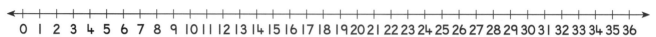

a $6 \bigcirc 3 = 2$ $6 \bigcirc 3 = 18$ b $6 \bigcirc 2 = 3$ $6 \bigcirc 3 = 9$

c $18 \bigcirc 9 = 9$ $18 \bigcirc 9 = 2$ d $18 \bigcirc 2 = 9$ $18 \bigcirc 9 = 27$

e $12 \bigcirc 3 = 9$ $12 \bigcirc 3 = 15$ f $12 \bigcirc 3 = 4$ $12 \bigcirc 3 = 36$

g $5 \bigcirc 5 = 10$ $5 \bigcirc 5 = 0$ h $5 \bigcirc 5 = 25$ $5 \bigcirc 5 = 1$

Multiplication and division game

Fill in = (equal to) or ≠ (not equal to) to make each sentence true.
Start at the bottom of the rocket and work your way up. The first
one to finish is the winner of the game!

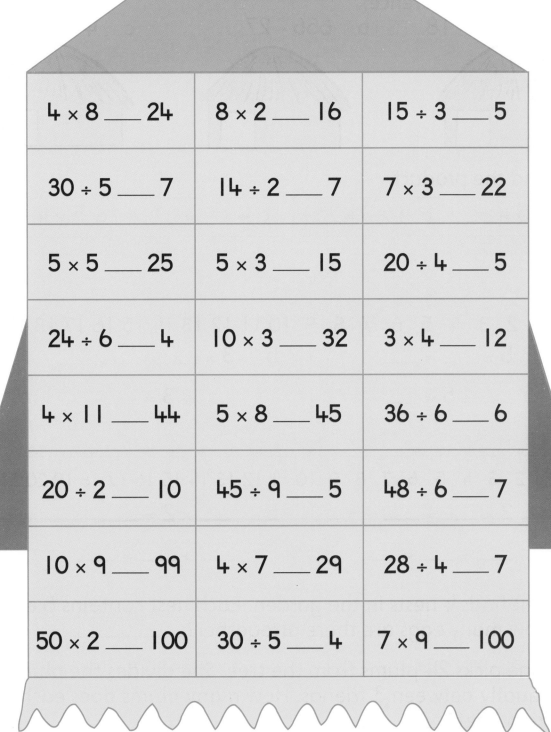

4 × 8 ___ 24	8 × 2 ___ 16	15 ÷ 3 ___ 5
30 ÷ 5 ___ 7	14 ÷ 2 ___ 7	7 × 3 ___ 22
5 × 5 ___ 25	5 × 3 ___ 15	20 ÷ 4 ___ 5
24 ÷ 6 ___ 4	10 × 3 ___ 32	3 × 4 ___ 12
4 × 11 ___ 44	5 × 8 ___ 45	36 ÷ 6 ___ 6
20 ÷ 2 ___ 10	45 ÷ 9 ___ 5	48 ÷ 6 ___ 7
10 × 9 ___ 99	4 × 7 ___ 29	28 ÷ 4 ___ 7
50 × 2 ___ 100	30 ÷ 5 ___ 4	7 × 9 ___ 100

More operations

1   Find the sum. Write the number on the hut.
   a   164 + 216   b   823 + 118 + 142   c   225 + 18 + 36

   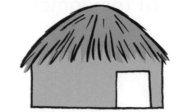   

2   Find the difference.
   a   834 – 18   b   656 – 27   c   498 – 9

3   Find the product.

| a 3 × 5 = _____ | b 4 × 3 = _____ | c 4 × 4 = _____ | d 5 × 4 = _____ |

4

```
 0  1  2  3  4  5  6  7  8  9  10 11 12 13 14 15 16 17 18 19 20
```

   a   5 × _____ = _____   b   3 × _____ = _____

       _____ ÷ 5 = _____   _____ ÷ 3 = _____

5

```
 0  1  2  3  4  5  6  7  8  9  10 11 12 13 14 15 16 17 18 19 20 21 22
```

   a   2 × _____ = _____   b   _____ × 2 = _____

       _____ ÷ _____ = _____   _____ ÷ _____ = _____

6   Neil finds 4 nests in the garden. Each nest contains 6 eggs.
   How many eggs are there altogether? _____

7   Jane picks 24 plums from the tree. She divides the plums
   equally between 3 friends. How many plums does each
   friend get? _____

Comparing litre amounts

1 Fill in <, > or = to make each number sentence true.

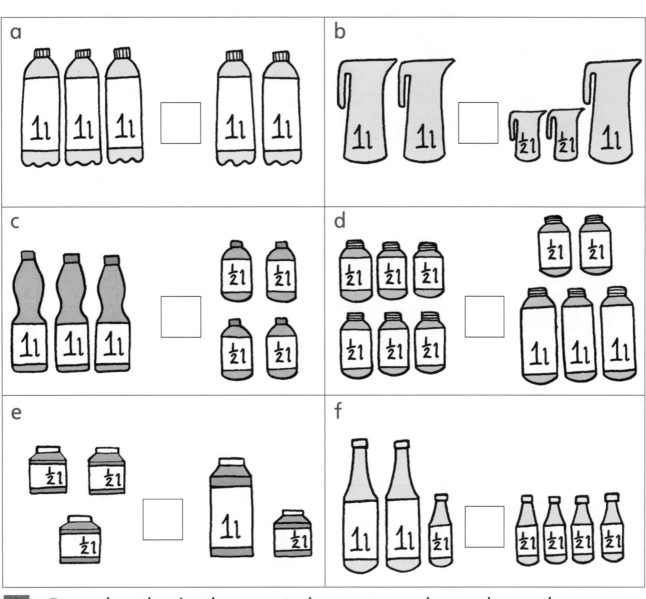

2 Draw bottles in the empty boxes to make each number sentence true.

a [ ] > [ ]

b [ ] < [ ]

Time on the hour and half-hour

1 Write the times shown on each clock.

seven o'clock _____ half past eight _____
7:00

_____ _____ _____ _____

2 Circle the correct time and write it in words.

11:30 11:00 10:30   7:30 6:30 6:00   12:00 12:30 1:00   6:30 5:30 6:00

_____ _____ _____ _____

7:30 7:00 12:00   4:00 4:30 3:30   12:00 6:00 12:30   3:30 3:00 9:30

_____ _____ _____ _____

Time on the quarter-hour

- Fold a circle in half, then into quarters.
- Use your quarter-circle to help you draw the **times** on the clocks below.
- Fill in the missing times using numbers or words.

Example

quarter to five

$\frac{1}{4}$ to 5

a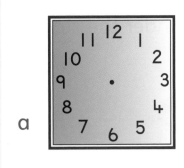

quarter past six

_____

b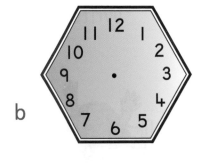

_____

$\frac{1}{4}$ to 12

c

quarter to two

_____

d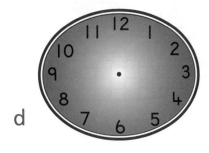

quarter past eleven

_____

e

_____

$\frac{1}{4}$ past 8

a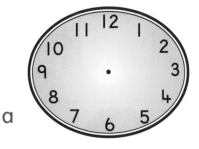

quarter to three

_____

g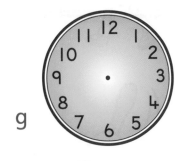

quarter to seven

_____

h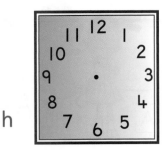

_____

$\frac{1}{4}$ past 1

Quarter past, quarter to

Jane wakes up at quarter past seven. She goes to school at quarter to eight. The bell rings for break at quarter past ten. At quarter past one, it is time for lunch. At quarter to three, she goes to play cricket with her friends. At quarter to seven, she eats dinner.

I a Match the pictures with the correct times from the story.
  b Write the times under the clock faces.

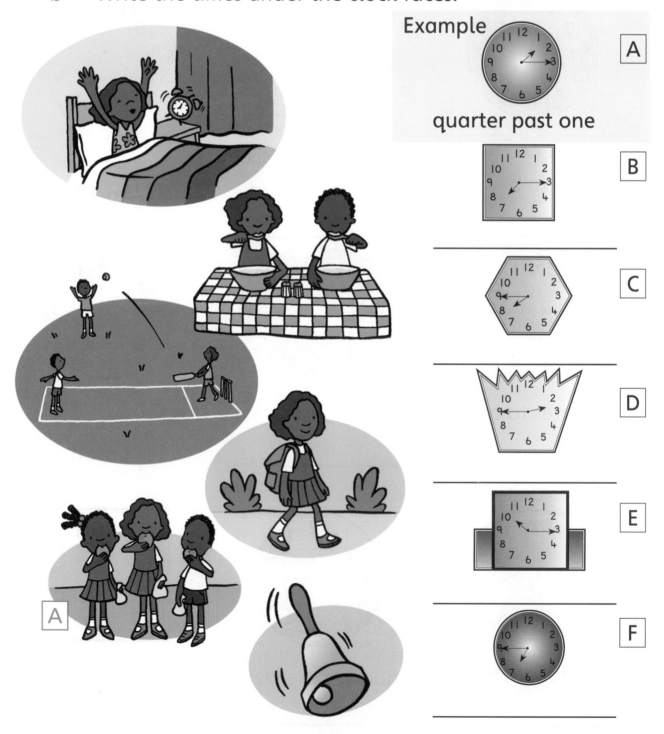

Example

A

quarter past one

B

C

D

E

A

F

Telling time in 5-minute intervals

1 Draw the hands.

five past two   twenty to five   ten past eleven   ten to twelve

2 Fill in the numbers around the clock to show the minutes.

3 Fill in the gaps.

There are ___ minutes in 1 hour. There are ___ minutes in half an hour. There are ___ minutes in a quarter of an hour.

 Five past 9
5 minutes past 9
9:05

  Twenty past 10
20 minutes past 10
10:20

4 Write these times in three ways.

_____   _____   _____

_____   _____   _____

_____   _____   _____

_____   _____   _____

_____   _____   _____

_____   _____   _____

Fractions – part of a set

1 What fraction of each set is shaded?

a    b   c    d

___   ___   ___   ___

2 Circle the fraction that tells what part of the set is shaded.

a

b

$\frac{1}{3}$ $\frac{3}{4}$ $\frac{11}{43}$ $\frac{2}{9}$ $\frac{6}{9}$ $\frac{1}{3}$ $\frac{2}{9}$ $\frac{6}{9}$

c

d

$\frac{3}{5}$ $\frac{2}{5}$ $\frac{2}{3}$ $\frac{2}{6}$ $\frac{2}{7}$ $\frac{5}{7}$

3

a Draw **4** circles. Shade half of them.	b Draw **3** triangles. Shade $\frac{2}{3}$ of them.
c Draw **6** donuts. Shade $\frac{1}{3}$ of them.	d Draw **5** hearts. Shade $\frac{3}{5}$ of them.

Unit fractions

$\frac{1}{4}$ of 20

To find a fraction, we use division.

$20 \div 4 = 5$

$\frac{1}{4}$ of 20 = 5

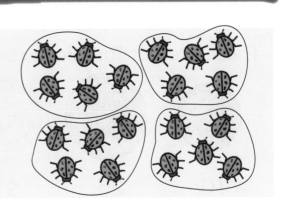

1 Circle groups to help you divide.

a

$\frac{1}{2}$ of 8 = ___

b

$\frac{1}{3}$ of 15 = ___

c

$\frac{1}{2}$ of 20 = ___

d

$\frac{1}{3}$ of 9 = ___

e

$\frac{1}{4}$ of 24 = ___

f

$\frac{1}{3}$ of 21 = ___

2 Use division to help you work out these.

a $36 \div 6 =$ ___ $42 \div 7 =$ ___ $30 \div 5 =$ ___

$\frac{1}{6}$ of 36 = ___   b $\frac{1}{7}$ of 42 = ___   c $\frac{1}{5}$ of 30 = ___

d $14 \div 7 =$ ___ $28 \div 4 =$ ___ $8 \div 3 =$ ___

$\frac{1}{7}$ of 14 = ___   e $\frac{1}{4}$ of 28 = ___   f $\frac{1}{3}$ of 18 = ___

3 Mum bought 16 plums. She gave Shauna a quarter of the plums. How many plums did Shauna get? ___

4 Gary sold half of his marbles. He still has 8 left. How many did he have to start with? ___

Coins

These are our Jamaican coins.

| 10c | 25c | $1 | $5 | $10 | $20 |

1 Calculate the total value of each set of coins. The first one has been done for you.

a	$10 $5 25c 25c	$15.50
b	$10 $20 25c 10c	
c	$5 $10 $1 25c 10c	
d	$5 $10 $20 $1 25c 10c	
e	25c 25c 10c 10c 10c 10c 10c	
f	$1 $1 $10 $5 $20 $20	

2 Draw your own coins to show $100.

Problem-solving

Write the number sentence and solve.

1 Janette bought ice-cream for $40 and plums for $90.

a How much did she spend altogether?

_____

b If she paid with $200, how much change did she get?

_____

2 John gave Ryan and Suelan 6 marbles each. He had
10 marbles left. How many did he have to start off with?

_____

3 Joy bought patties for $60 and drinks for $30. She paid
with a $100 note. How much change did she get?

_____

4 I had 22 sweets. I ate 4 and gave 6 to my sister.
How many sweets do I have left?

_____

5 Joanne drew 20 butterflies. She shaded 4 red and 9 green.
How many were still unshaded?

_____

6 A woman wants to give 12 children one patty and a soda
each. She buys 10 patties and 8 sodas.
How many more sodas and patties should she buy?
Do a drawing to help you work out the answer.

_____

Using money

a   Lulu bought an ice-cream and a lollipop. She paid _____.

b   Mike bought a T-shirt and a beach ball. He paid _____.

c   Bella bought **2** ice-creams. She paid _____.

d   Joan bought **2** lollipops. Her change from **$50** was _____.

e   Alan had **$200**. He bought an ice-cream and a hula-hoop.
     What else could he buy? _____

f   Ray had **$200**. He bought a T-shirt. What else could he buy?

     _____

g   Pat bought a chocolate bar and a beach bat. She spent
     _____. Her change from **$150** was _____.

h   Penny bought an ice-cream, a hula-hoop and a beach ball.
     She spent _____. Her change from **$400** was _____.

Making change

  To work out the change from $1.00, imagine changing the dollar into coins so you can pay with exactly 75c.

$1.00 =

Pay with

You have change.

1 Find the total cost of each set.

a  _____

b $55 $35 _____

c $40 $55 _____

d $55 $20 $16 _____

e $40 $30 _____

f $32 $25 $42 _____

2 Draw the coins you would use to pay the exact price. Draw the coins that would be left in change from $100.

$8	$6	$35	$45	$85	$70
Pay with:	Pay with:	Pay with:	Pay with:	Pay with:	Pay with:
Change left:	Change left:	Change left:	Change left:	Change left:	Change left:

Calculating with money

I   Write the number sentence. Work out the total cost of each set of items. Check your answers with a calculator.

a

___ + ___ = ___

b

___ + ___ = ___

c
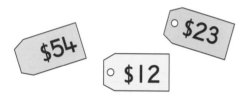
___ + ___ + ___ = ___

d

___ + ___ = ___

e

___ + ___ = ___

f
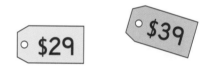
___ + ___ = ___

g

___ + ___ = ___

h
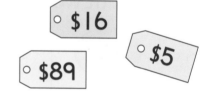
___ + ___ + ___ = ___

i

___ + ___ + ___ = ___

j

___ + ___ + ___ = ___

Spending money

Donkey Ride	$30	Disco	$20
Haunted House	$20	Bingo	$50
Face Painting	$10	Lucky Dip	$40

1. Ella went to the fair. She went on a donkey ride. Then she went to the disco. She also had her face painted. How much did she spend?

   ___ + ___ + ___ = ___

2. Mr Joe took his 4 children to the disco. How much did he pay for their tickets?

   ___ × ___ = ___

3. Danny went on 3 donkey rides. How much did he pay?

   ___ × ___ = ___

4. 25 children went into the haunted house. How much did they pay altogether?

   ___ × ___ = ___

Find the word

1 Find and circle these words in the grid. Tick off the words as you find them. One has been done for you.

fraction	even	**odd**	dozen	empty set
add	multiply ✓	**plus**	cuboid	**sphere**
square	perimeter	divide	subtract	symmetry

h	r	m	u	l	t	i	p	l	y	d	r	w	s	f
p	e	r	i	m	e	t	e	r	w	e	r	f	v	e
y	u	h	g	d	w	f	r	a	c	t	i	o	n	g
e	r	n	h	e	m	p	t	y	s	e	t	m	d	n
h	v	b	f	g	c	u	b	o	i	d	t	h	j	k
v	n	g	t	d	s	a	d	i	v	i	d	e	e	f
o	d	d	n	h	b	t	f	h	u	i	k	h	d	w
b	h	y	u	m	d	s	p	h	e	r	e	e	g	t
h	p	l	u	s	b	t	y	u	x	d	r	e	h	i
r	v	b	s	u	b	t	r	a	c	t	n	j	r	e
b	h	y	r	e	h	e	v	e	n	n	u	y	t	f
f	r	y	l	s	q	u	a	r	e	g	t	r	d	p
q	v	f	r	y	n	h	s	y	m	m	e	t	r	y
p	w	s	l	v	r	m	d	o	z	e	n	m	u	y
t	j	h	t	y	a	d	d	n	u	y	f	r	k	l

1   The letters a, e, i, o and u are called vowels.
    Here are four children's names:
    Joseph Green   Roshane Francis
    Shelley Greenwood   Suzette Pryce
    Count the vowels in the names above. Make a tally mark in
    the table for each vowel that you count.

Vowel	Tally	Total number
a		
e		
i		
o		
u		

a   The vowel that occurs most often is ___.
b   The vowel that occurs least often is ___.

2   Write the names of four children from your class.

    Name 1: _____   Name 2: _____

    Name 3: _____   Name 4: _____

    Tally the vowels in their names and fill in the table.

Vowel	Tally	Total number
a		
e		
i		
o		
u		

a   The vowel that occurs most often is ___.
b   The vowel that occurs least often is ___.

3   Compare the results from the two tables. What do you notice?

Collecting data about living things

I Each living thing lives and grows best in a particular kind of place. This place is called its habitat.

Habitats of living things						
House	In the ground	In water	On other animals	On a farm	In trees or nests	In big open spaces
People	Moles	Lilies	Ticks	Goats	Birds	Lions
Pets	Worms	Fish	Fleas	Pigs	Bees	Tigers
	Trees	Turtles	Lice	Chickens	Spiders	Elephants

a Name three animals that live on farms.

_____   _____   _____

b Name three animals that live on other animals.

_____   _____   _____

c In what sort of habitat do tigers live?

_____

d Add three more living things to each habitat in the table. Fill in your answers on the table.

Do you think it is possible to list all living things in a table like this? Why or why not?

Using data

Temperature in Kingston over a week

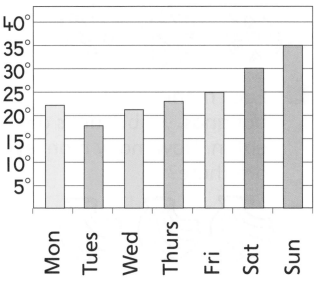

Icicle sales in Kingston over the same week

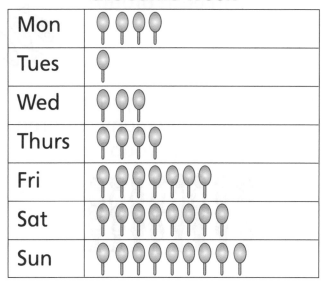

🥄 = 10 icicles

1   a   The coolest day of the week was _____.

    b   The hottest day of the week was _____.

    c   The temperature dropped between _____ and _____.

    d   How much hotter was it on Sunday
        than on Tuesday?   _____.

2   a   The most icicles were sold on _____.

    b   The fewest icicles were sold on _____.

    c   _____ icicles were sold on the weekend.

3   Do you think the sales of icicles were rounded off? _____.
    Give reasons for your answer.

    _____

4   a   How many icicles were sold on the hottest day?   ____

    b   How many icicles were sold on the coolest day?   ____

    c   What do you notice about the icicle sales and
        the temperature? _____

Unit 29 Division

There are 12 fish. Put the fish into 4 equal groups. How many fish are in each group?

12 ÷ 4 = ___

12 ÷ 4 = 3

1 16 children play in 4 equal groups. How many children are in each group?

___ ÷ ___ = ___

2 Each monkey eats 3 bananas. 15 bananas get eaten. How many monkeys are there?

___ ÷ ___ = ___

3 18 eggs are sold at the market. Each customer buys 6 eggs. How many customers buy eggs?

___ ÷ ___ = ___

4 The carpenter buys 20 chair legs. There are 4 legs on each chair. How many chairs can she build?

___ ÷ ___ = ___

5 Draw groups of shapes to help you work out these.

a   16 ÷ 4 = ___   b   15 ÷ 3 = ___   c   18 ÷ 6 = ___

d   12 ÷ 2 = ___   e   18 ÷ 3 = ___   f   20 ÷ 4 = ___

g   12 ÷ 4 = ___   h   10 ÷ 5 = ___   i   16 ÷ 2 = ___

Division

How many times does 5 go into 15?

15 ÷ 5 = _____

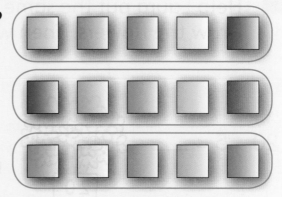

There are 15 squares.
Put the squares into groups of 5.
There are 3 groups.

15 ÷ 5 = 3

1   Each packet of seeds is a different size. The gardener wants the same number of seeds in each row. Draw the correct number of seeds in each row. Then write the number sentence.

	● ● ● ● ● ● ● ● ● ● ● ● ● ● ● ● ● ●	18 ÷ 2 = 9
		21 ÷ ☐ = ☐
		16 ÷ ☐ = ☐
		☐ ÷ 9 = ☐
		☐ ÷ 3 = ☐
		☐ ÷ ☐ = ☐

● = 1 seed

2   Draw your own shapes on paper to help you work out these.

a   18 ÷ 6 = _____   b   20 ÷ 10 = _____   c   27 ÷ 3 = _____

d   16 ÷ 2 = _____   e   28 ÷ 4 = _____   f   27 ÷ 9 = _____

g   30 ÷ 6 = _____   h   22 ÷ 2 = _____   i   30 ÷ 10 = _____

j   24 ÷ 4 = _____   k   21 ÷ 3 = _____   l   36 ÷ 3 = _____

Division

1 Help Laura put the same number of flowers in each vase. Draw the flowers. Then write the answer.

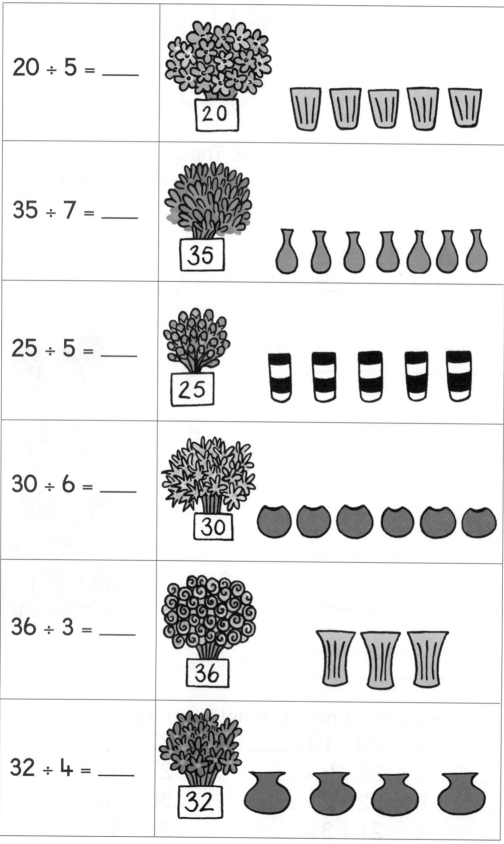

20 ÷ 5 = ___	
35 ÷ 7 = ___	
25 ÷ 5 = ___	
30 ÷ 6 = ___	
36 ÷ 3 = ___	
32 ÷ 4 = ___	

Division

1   Draw your own groups to work out these.

a 22 ÷ 2 = ___	b 30 ÷ 5 = ___	c 32 ÷ 4 = ___
d 20 ÷ 2 = ___	e 28 ÷ 7 = ___	f 20 ÷ 4 = ___
g 36 ÷ 4 = ___	h 26 ÷ 2 = ___	i 28 ÷ 4 = ___
j 20 ÷ 10 = ___	k 36 ÷ 9 = ___	l 21 ÷ 3 = ___

How can you use multiplying to help you check your answers to division problems?

Division by subtracting

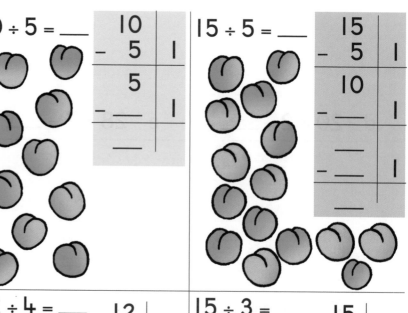

$6 \times 2 = 2 + 2 + 2 + 2 + 2 + 2 = 12$

$6 \div 2 =$ ___

Work it out by subtracting 2s.

Take away 2.　　4 left.

Take away 2.　　2 left.

Take away 2.　　0 left.

We took away 3 groups of 2.

So $6 \div 2 = 3$.

6	
− 2	1
4	
− 2	1
2	
− 2	1
0	3

1　Complete these.

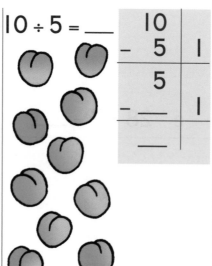

$12 \div 3 =$ ___

12	
− 3	1
9	
− 3	1
6	
− 3	1
3	
− 3	1
0	4

$10 \div 5 =$ ___

10	
− 5	1
5	
− ___	1
___	

$15 \div 5 =$ ___

15	
− 5	1
10	
− ___	1
___	
− ___	1
___	

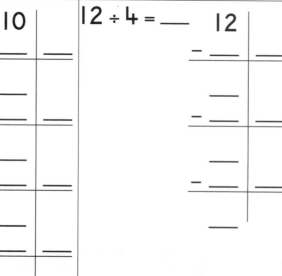

$10 \div 2 =$ ___

10

$12 \div 4 =$ ___

12

$15 \div 3 =$ ___

15

Division

$8 \div 2 =$ ___

There are **8** hats.
Put the hats into groups of **2**.
There are **4** groups of **2**.
$8 \div 2 = 4$

1   Some fishermen caught **14** fish.
Each fisherman caught **7** fish.
How many fishermen were there?

___ $\div$ ___ = ___

2   A woman sold **18** pineapples at
the market. Each customer bought
3 pineapples. How many people
bought pineapples?

___ $\div$ ___ = ___

3   **10** plums were eaten. Each child
ate **2** plums. How many children ate
plums?

___ $\div$ ___ = ___

4   Some children shared **12** bananas.
Each child had **4** bananas. How
many children were there?

___ $\div$ ___ = ___

5   Divide without using shapes.

a $12 \div 3 =$ ___   b $120 \div 5 =$ ___   c $220 \div 4 =$ ___

d $21 \div 7 =$ ___   e $12 \div 2 =$ ___   f $127 \div 3 =$ ___

g $624 \div 6 =$ ___   h $618 \div 2 =$ ___   i $416 \div 4 =$ ___

j $416 \div 2 =$ ___   k $814 \div 2 =$ ___   l $624 \div 3 =$ ___

m $27 \div 9 =$ ___   n $824 \div 4 =$ ___   o $128 \div 4 =$ ___

Division on a number line

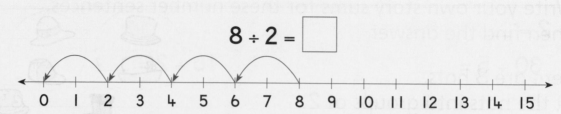

$8 \div 2 = \boxed{}$

Start at 8 and make groups of 2 until you reach 0.
There are 4 groups of 2. $8 \div 2 = 4$

1   Draw the groups and complete the number sentences.

a $15 \div 3 = \underline{}$

b $14 \div 2 = \underline{}$

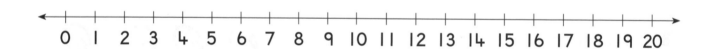

c $16 \div 4 = \underline{}$

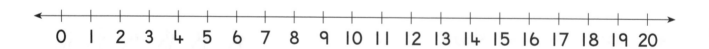

d $20 \div 5 = \underline{}$

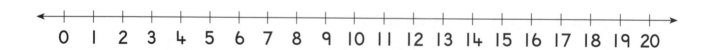

2   Work out these. Make number lines to help you.

a $22 \div 2 = \underline{}$ b $25 \div 5 = \underline{}$ c $12 \div 1 = \underline{}$ d $18 \div 3 = \underline{}$

e $20 \div 2 = \underline{}$ f $20 \div 10 = \underline{}$ g $20 \div 5 = \underline{}$ h $15 \div 5 = \underline{}$

Looking back

1 Write your own story sums for these number sentences.
Then find the answer.

a   30 ÷ 5 = ___

b   16 ÷ 2 = ___

_____

_____

_____

_____

2 Choose five foods for a survey. Find out which is the favourite food of children in your class. Record your information in the table below. Then show the information in a bar graph.

Food	Tally	Number

3 Help the baker to work out how many cakes and cookies she can make.

I lemon cake needs 2 lemons.	I have 18 lemons.	How many cakes can I make? ___ ÷ ___ = ___
1 cookie needs 8 chocolate chips.	I have 48 choc chips.	How many cookies can I make? ___ ÷ ___ = ___
I cake needs 4 eggs.	I have 24 eggs.	How many cakes can I make? ___ ÷ ___ = ___

Looking back

4 Fill in the hands.

8:30

$\frac{1}{4}$ to 8

quarter past nine

seven o'clock

12:00

$\frac{1}{4}$ past 11

half past three

$\frac{1}{4}$ to 9

5 Write true or false for each number sentence.

a $45 \div 5 = 9$ _____

b $6 \times 5 = 25$ _____

c $16 + 5 = 21$ _____

d $18 - 9 = 9$ _____

e $40 - 15 = 25$ _____

f $7 \times 6 = 42$ _____

g $35 \div 7 = 6$ _____

6 Fill in = or ≠.

a 4×8 ___ 40

b $25 \div 5$ ___ 5

c 4×7 ___ 28

d 3×5 ___ 15

e $16 \div 4$ ___ 4

f $30 \div 5$ ___ 5

g $28 \div 7$ ___ 4

7 Find these.

a $\frac{1}{2}$ of 16 = ___

b $\frac{1}{3}$ of 15 = ___

c $\frac{1}{5}$ of 25 = ___

d $\frac{1}{4}$ of 16 = ___

e $\frac{1}{3}$ of 21 = ___

f $\frac{1}{6}$ of 18 = ___

Number patterns

1	2	3	4	5	6	7	8	9	10
11	12	13	14	15	16	17	18	19	20
21	22	23	24	25	26	27	28	29	30
31	32	33	34	35	36	37	38	39	40
41	42	43	44	45	46	47	48	49	50
51	52	53	54	55	56	57	58	59	60
61	62	63	64	65	66	67	68	69	70
71	72	73	74	75	76	77	78	79	80
81	82	83	84	85	86	87	88	89	90
91	92	93	94	95	96	97	98	99	100

1 Use the chart above and follow these instructions.

a Circle in red the numbers whose digits have a difference of 1 (e.g. 23 because $3 - 2 = 1$).

b Circle in blue the number that is the sum of 10 and 5.

c Circle in green the number that is the answer to $35 \div 5$.

d Shade in red the number that has 5 tens and 4 ones.

e Shade in yellow all the numbers with 6 in the tens place.

f Draw a triangle around all the numbers with 9 in the ones place.

g Draw a star around the numbers whose digits add up to ten.

2 Which numbers have a circle and a star around them?

_____

3 Which numbers have a red circle and are shaded yellow?

_____

4 Which numbers have a star and are shaded yellow?

_____

5 Draw a square around all the numbers whose tens digit is larger than their ones digit. What pattern do you notice?

Naming polygons

We name polygons by the points at the ends of their sides. Each side is named by the points at each end of the line segment that makes that side.

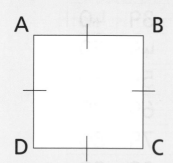

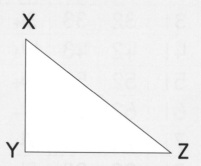

Square ABCD
Sides: AB = BC = CD = DA = 3 cm
The short lines tell us that
the sides are equal in length.

Triangle XYZ
Sides: XY = 3 cm,
YZ = 4 cm and
ZX = 5 cm.

I Say whether each shape is a triangle, square or rectangle. Name the shape and write the measurement of each side.

a

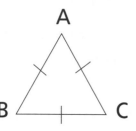

b

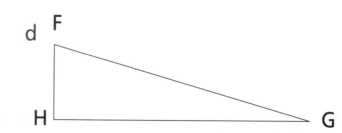

c

d

Probability

Probability is the chance of something happening.
Some things are more likely to happen than others.

 A coin has two sides. When you flip a coin,
the coin will land on heads or on tails. Both
outcomes are equally likely.

 This arrow is more likely to land on the red than
on the blue. This is because there is more red
than blue.

1 What do you think will happen when you spin each arrow?
Look at each spinner and complete the statements. Write
more likely, **equally likely** or **less likely** for each. Give a
reason for your answer.

a  The arrow is _____ to land on yellow
than on blue, but it is _____ to land
on red because _____.

b 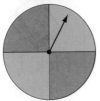 The arrow is _____ to land on red as
on green because _____.

2 Fill in **more likely**, **equally likely** or **less likely**.

a  The arrow is _____ to land on green
than on blue, but is _____ to land
on green than on red.

b  The arrow is _____ to land on green
as on blue, but it is _____ to land on
red than on green or blue.

c 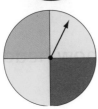 The arrow is _____ to land on blue
or on green, but it is _____ to land
on yellow.

Probability

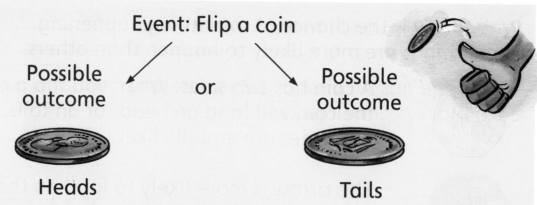

Event: Flip a coin

Possible outcome → or ← Possible outcome

Heads   Tails

Each event is equally likely to happen.

The probability of throwing heads is 1 out of 2 = $\frac{1}{2}$.

The probability of throwing tails is 1 out of 2 = $\frac{1}{2}$.

If you throw a coin 10 times, how many times is it likely to land on heads?

$\frac{1}{2}$ of 10 = 5

It is likely to land on heads 5 out of 10 times.

1   Complete the table.

Event	Flip a coin	Throw a dice	Spin the spinner	Pick 1 card from a pack of 52
Number of possible outcomes	____	____	____	____
What is the probability of:	landing on heads? ____	throwing a six? ____	landing on red? ____	picking a 3 of ♥? ____

2   a   If you flip a 10c coin 20 times, it is likely to show heads ____ times and tails ____ times.

     b   If you flip the coin 50 times, it is likely to show heads ____ times and tails ____ times.

Measuring with square units

We use square units to work out the area
of a shape.

This shape has an area of 12 square units.
Each block is one unit.

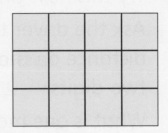

1 How many blocks make up the area of each shape?

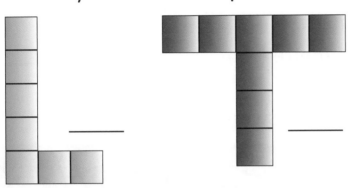

2 Estimate the area of each of these curved shapes.

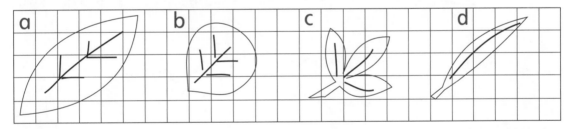

3 Look at this towel. Work out the area
taken up by each colour.
Write the answers in the table.

Colour	Number of square units
Red	
Blue	
Green	
Yellow	
Purple	

Working with km

1. Try this next time you travel by car.

   Ask the driver to show you the starting distance on the odometer. Record the last two digits. ____

   What is one more than this number? ____

   Note when the odometer reaches the next number – this happens after you have travelled a kilometre.

   Complete the statement.

   We travelled one kilometre from _____ to _____.

2. Use the map to find the answers.

   a   From the church to the school is about ____ km.

   b   The distance from the school to Mandy's house is about ____ km.

   c   John walks from school to the post office and on to Mandy's house. How many kilometres does he walk?

   _____

   d   Amina is walking from the shop to the post office. Halfway there she gets a lift from a friend. How far did she walk?

   _____

Unit 34 Division at work

At the market, the grocer has to fit the fruit into boxes. The table tells you how many fit into a box. Count the number of each fruit that was delivered. Work out how many boxes the grocer can fill from today's delivery. Use repeated subtraction to work out your answers, using the pictures to help you.

Fruit	Number in each box	Delivered today	Number of boxes
mango	12		3
pineapple	5		
apple	9		
watermelon	2		
peach	8		
pear	11		

Division problems

Nelly has 15 seedlings. She plants 5 seedlings in each pot. How many pots does she need?

She takes away 3 groups of 5 seedlings. She needs 3 pots.
$15 \div 5 = 3$

```
 15
- 5 | 1
 10
- 5 | 1
  5
- 5 | 1
  0   3
```

1   The florist puts 10 roses in each bunch.

   a   On Monday, she gets a delivery of 30 roses. How many bunches of roses can she make on Monday? ____

   b   On Tuesday, she gets a delivery of 70 roses. How many bunches of roses can she make on Tuesday? ____

2   The florist puts 7 poppies in each bunch.

   a   On Wednesday, she gets a delivery of 28 poppies. How many bunches of poppies can she make on Wednesday?

       ____

   b   On Thursday, she gets a delivery of 42 poppies. How many bunches of poppies can she make on Thursday?

       ____

3   The florist puts 5 tulips in each bunch.

   a   On Friday, she gets a delivery of 135 tulips. How many bunches of tulips can she make on Friday? ____

   b   On Saturday, she gets a delivery of 425 tulips. How many bunches of tulips can she make on Saturday? ____

4   How many bunches of flowers did the florist make altogether from Monday to Saturday? ____

Dividing bigger numbers

Laura has 162 beads. She wants to make 3 necklaces, each with the same number of beads. She needs to divide the beads into equal groups. $162 \div 3 = ?$ 162 is the **dividend**. 3 is the **divisor**. Laura needs to find the **quotient**.

```
    5 4
3 | 1 6 2
   -1 5 ↓
      1 2
```

$16 \div 3 = 5$ remainder 1
$5 \times 3 = 15$
$12 \div 3 = 4$

Here is another example. $288 \div 4 = ?$

```
      7 2
4 | 2 8 8
   -2 8 ↓
      0 8
```

$28 \div 4 = 7$
$8 \div 4 = 2$
$288 \div 4 = 72$

1 Find the quotient.

a $3 \overline{) 636}$ b $2 \overline{) 422}$ c $3 \overline{) 396}$

d $5 \overline{) 155}$ e $3 \overline{) 126}$ f $4 \overline{) 128}$

g $3 \overline{) 216}$ h $4 \overline{) 208}$ i $3 \overline{) 210}$

More division with bigger numbers

Mr Abrahams gives $4 880 to his four children. They share the money equally between them. How much does each child get?

$4 880 ÷ 4 = ?

$$\begin{array}{r} 1220 \\ 4\overline{\smash{\big)}\,4880} \end{array}$$

Each child gets $1220.

1 Find the quotient.

a $2\overline{\smash{\big)}\,24}$

b $3\overline{\smash{\big)}\,360}$

c $4\overline{\smash{\big)}\,436}$

d $3\overline{\smash{\big)}\,2436}$

e $5\overline{\smash{\big)}\,2055}$

f $6\overline{\smash{\big)}\,2466}$

2 Malcom used 436 bricks to build 4 flower beds, each with the same number of bricks. How many bricks did he use for each flower bed?

3 A woman gave $2 768 to her 2 daughters. They shared the money equally between them. How much money did each daughter get?

4 1 550 cyclists entered a cycle race. The organisers divided the cyclists into 5 groups. How many cyclists were in each group?

Multiplying and dividing

1 The white rabbit can jump **2** spaces at a time. Draw the jumps it makes to reach the carrot. Fill in the number sentences.

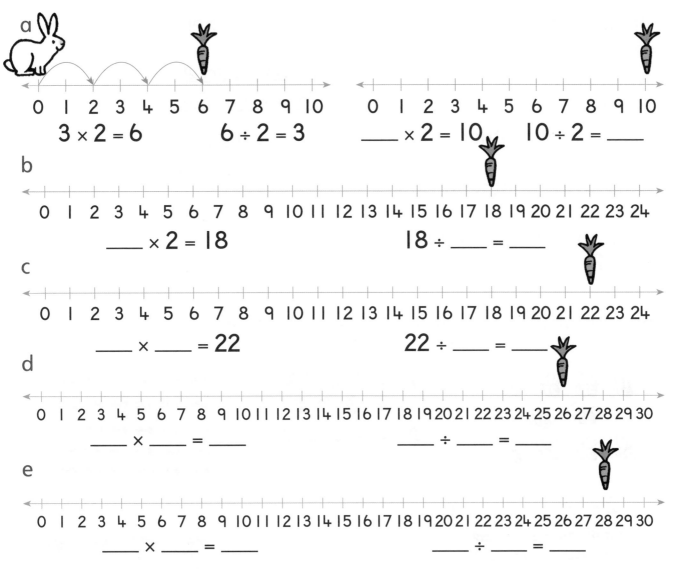

a

0 1 2 3 4 5 6 7 8 9 10

$3 \times 2 = 6$ $6 \div 2 = 3$

0 1 2 3 4 5 6 7 8 9 10

___ $\times 2 = 10$ $10 \div 2 =$ ___

b

0 1 2 3 4 5 6 7 8 9 10 11 12 13 14 15 16 17 18 19 20 21 22 23 24

___ $\times 2 = 18$ $18 \div$ ___ $=$ ___

c

0 1 2 3 4 5 6 7 8 9 10 11 12 13 14 15 16 17 18 19 20 21 22 23 24

___ $\times$ ___ $= 22$ $22 \div$ ___ $=$ ___

d

0 1 2 3 4 5 6 7 8 9 10 11 12 13 14 15 16 17 18 19 20 21 22 23 24 25 26 27 28 29 30

___ $\times$ ___ $=$ ___   ___ $\div$ ___ $=$ ___

e

0 1 2 3 4 5 6 7 8 9 10 11 12 13 14 15 16 17 18 19 20 21 22 23 24 25 26 27 28 29 30

___ $\times$ ___ $=$ ___   ___ $\div$ ___ $=$ ___

2 The black rabbit jumps **3** places at a time. The spotted rabbit jumps **4** places at a time. Draw both rabbits' jumps on each number line. Write the number sentence and say who lands on the carrot.

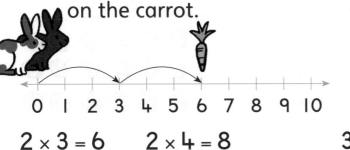

0 1 2 3 4 5 6 7 8 9 10

$2 \times 3 = 6$ $2 \times 4 = 8$

The black rabbit lands
on the carrot.

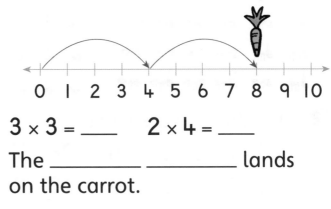

0 1 2 3 4 5 6 7 8 9 10

$3 \times 3 =$ ___ $2 \times 4 =$ ___

The _____ _____ lands
on the carrot.